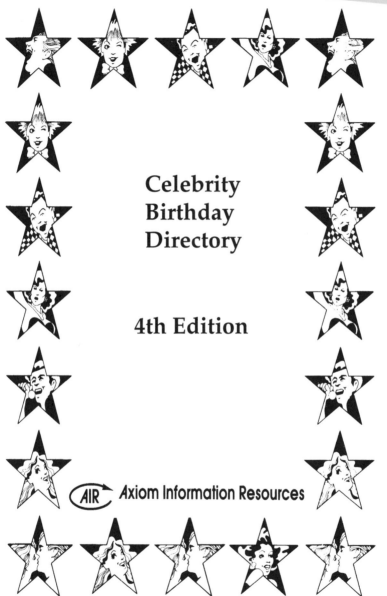

Celebrity Birthday Directory

4th Edition

 Axiom Information Resources

Celebrity Birthday Directory™
Published by Axiom Information Resources
Ann Arbor, Michigan 48107 USA

Copyright © 1997 Axiom Information Resources

Published by:
Axiom Information Resources
P.O. Box 8015
Ann Arbor, MI 48107

Printed in USA
ISBN #0-943213-26-6
Library of Congress Catalog Card Number 95-77298

SPECIAL SALES
The Celebrity Birthday Directory™ is
available at special quantity discounts
for bulk purchases. For information write:

Axiom Information Resources
P.O. Box 8015-T6
Ann Arbor, MI 48107

A

Hank Aaron	2/5/34
George Abbott	6/25/1887
Jim Abbott	9/19/67
Philip Abbott	3/20/24
William "Budd" Abbott	10/2/00
Paula Abdul	4/19/62
Kareem Abdul-Jabbar	4/16/47
Walter Abel	6/6/1898
Ralph Abernathy	3/11/26
F. Murray Abraham	10/24/39
Creighton Abrams	9/15/44
Bella Abzug	7/24/20
Dean Acheson	4/11/1893
Sharon Acker	4/2/35
Betty Ackerman	2/29/28
Peter Ackroyd	10/5/49
Roy Acuff	9/15/03
Deborah Adair	5/23/52
Ansel Adams	2/20/02
Brooke Adams	2/8/49
Don Adams	4/19/27
Douglas Adams	3/11/52
Edie Adams	4/16/29
Franklin P. Adams	11/15/1881
Gerry Adams	10/6/48
Joey Adams	1/6/11
John Adams	10/30/1735
John Quincy Adams	7/11/1767
Julia Adams	10/17/28
Mason Adams	2/26/19
Maud Adams	2/12/45
Maude Adams	11/11/1872
Nick Adams	7/10/31
Samuel Adams	9/27/1722
Jay Adamson	1/20/00
Charles Addams	1/7/12
Dawn Addams	9/21/30
"Cannonball" Adderley	9/15/28
Herb Adderley	6/8/39

Wesley Addy	8/4/13
Rick Adelman	6/16/46
Isabella Adjani	6/27/55
Buddy Adler	6/22/09
Larry Adler	2/10/14
Luther Adler	6/4/03
Polly Adler	4/16/00
Renata Adler	10/19/38
Richard Adler	8/3/21
Stella Adler	2/10/02
Adolfo	2/15/33
Renee Adoree	9/30/1898
Adrian	3/3/03
Iris Adrian	5/29/13
Max Adrian	11/1/03
Andre Agassi	4/29/70
James Agee	11/27/09
Philip Agee	7/19/35
Spiro Agnew	11/9/18
Martin Agronsky	1/15/15
Mark Aguirre	12/10/59
Jenny Agutter	12/20/52
Brian Aherne	5/2/02
Danny Aiello	6/20/36
Conrad Aiken	8/5/1889
George Aiken	8/20/1892
Troy Aikman	11/21/66
Roger Ailes	5/15/40
Alvin Ailey	1/5/31
Anouk Aimee	4/27/34
Danny Ainge	3/17/59
Franklin Ajaye	5/13/49
Anna Akhmatova	6/23/1889
Emperor Akihito	12/23/33
Claude Akins	5/25/18
Joss Akland	2/29/28
Licia Albanese	7/22/13
Edward Albee	3/12/28
Eddie Albert	4/22/08
Edward Albert	2/20/51
Marv Albert	6/12/43
Prince Albert	3/14/58
Anna Marie Albertghetti	5/15/36
Jack Albertson	6/16/10

Hardie Albright	12/6/03	Kirstie Alley	1/12/55
Lola Albright	7/20/24	Sara Allgood	10/31/1883
Madeleine K. Albright	5/15/37	Bobby Allison	12/3/37
Amy Alcott	2/22/56	May Allison	6/14/1895
Alan Alda	1/28/36	Svetlana Alliuyeva	2/28/26
Robert Alda	2/26/14	Duane Allman	11/20/46
Theoni Aldredge	8/22/32	Greg Allman	12/8/47
Richard Aldrich	8/17/02	June Allyson	10/7/17
Edwin "Buzz" Aldrin	1/20/30	Roberto Alomar	2/5/68
Sholem Aleichem	2/18/1859	Sandy Alomar, Jr.	6/18/66
Alexander I	12/23/1777	Moises Alou	7/3/66
Alexander the Great	9/20/356 BC	Herb Alpert	3/31/35
Jane Alexander	10/28/39	Hollis Alpert	9/24/16
Jason Alexander	9/23/59	Joseph Alsop	10/11/10
Shana Alexander	10/6/25	Carol Alt	12/1/60
Kim Alexis	7/15/60	Robert B. Altman	2/20/25
Raul Alfonsin	3/12/27	Luis Alvarez	6/13/11
Horatio Alger	1/13/1832	Wilson Alvarez	3/24/70
Nelson Algrew	3/28/09	Jorge Amado	10/8/12
Muhammad Ali	1/17/42	Eric Ambler	6/28/09
Tatyana M. Ali	1/24/79	Don Ameche	5/31/08
Mary Alice	12/3/41	Ed Ames	7/9/27
Martine Allard	8/24/70	Leon Ames	1/20/03
Bob Allen	3/28/06	Hardy Amies	7/17/09
Byron Allen	4/22/62	Idi Amin	1/1/25
Chad Allen	6/5/74	Kingsley Amis	4/16/22
Debbie Allen	1/16/50	Cleveland Amory	9/2/17
Deborah Allen	9/30/53	John Amos	12/27/41
Dick Allen	3/8/42	Wally "Famous" Amos	7/1/36
Duane Allen	4/29/43	Morey Amsterdam	12/14/14
Elizabeth Allen	1/25/34	Hans Christian Andersen	4/2/1805
Eric Allen	11/22/65	Ib Andersen	12/14/54
Fred Allen	5/31/1894	Bibi Anderson	11/11/35
George Allen	4/29/22	Daryl Anderson	7/1/51
Gracie Allen	7/26/06	Eddie Anderson	9/18/05
Joan Allen	8/20/56	George "Sparky" Anderson	2/22/34
Karen Allen	10/5/51	Harry Anderson	10/14/52
Marcus Allen	3/26/60	Ian Anderson	8/10/47
Marty Allen	3/23/22	Jack Anderson	10/19/22
Mel Allen	2/14/13	John Anderson	2/15/22
Phillip Richard Allen	3/26/39	Judith Anderson	2/10/1898
Steve Allen	12/26/21	June Anderson	12/30/52
Tim Allen	6/13/53	Kenny Anderson	10/9/70
Woody Allen	12/1/35	Lindsay Anderson	4/17/23

Loni Anderson	8/5/46
Lynn Anderson	9/26/47
Marian Anderson	2/17/02
Maxwell Anderson	12/15/1888
Melissa Sue Anderson	9/26/62
Morten Anderson	8/19/60
Neal Anderson	8/14/64
O.J. Anderson	1/19/57
Richard Dean Anderson	1/23/50
Richard N. Anderson	8/8/26
Robert Anderson	4/28/17
Warner Anderson	3/10/11
Willie "Flipper" Anderson	3/7/67
Keith Andes	7/12/20
Ursula Andress	3/19/36
Mario Andretti	2/28/40
Prince Andrew	2/19/60
Anthony Andrews	1/12/48
Dana Andrews	1/1/09
Edward Andrews	10/9/14
Julie Andrews	10/1/35
Maxine Andrews	1/3/18
Patti Andrews	2/16/20
Yuri Andropov	6/14/14
Joaquin Andujar	12/21/52
Pier Angeli	6/19/32
Maya Angelou	4/4/28
Paul Anka	7/30/41
Evelyn Ankers	8/17/20
Ann-Margret	4/28/41
Annabella	7/14/12
Princess Anne	8/15/50
Walter Annenberg	3/13/08
Jean Anouilh	6/23/10
Michael Ansara	4/15/22
Adam Ant	11/3/54
Greg Anthony	11/15/67
Susan B. Anthony	2/15/1820
Marie Antoinette	11/2/1755
Susan Anton	10/12/50
Michelangelo Antonioni	9/29/12
Johnny Appleseed	9/26/1774
Corazon Aquino	1/25/33
Yasir Arafat	8/24/29

Fatty Arbuckle	3/24/1887
Diane Arbus	3/14/23
Eddie Arcaro	2/19/16
Anne Archer	8/25/47
Dennis Archer	1/1/42
Jeffrey Archer	4/14/40
Nate Archibald	9/2/48
Elizabeth Arden	12/31/1884
Eve Arden	4/30/12
Moshe Arens	12/27/25
Jimmy Arias	8/16/64
Ted Arison	2/24/24
Jean-Bertrand Aristide	7/15/53
Alan Arkin	3/26/34
Samuel Z. Arkoff	6/12/18
Roone Arledge	7/8/31
Harold Arlen	2/15/05
Richard Arlen	9/1/1899
George Arliss	4/10/1868
Giorgio Armani	7/11/34
Joan Armatrading	12/9/50
Pedro Armendariz	5/9/12
Richard Armour	7/15/06
Anne Armstrong	12/27/27
B.J. Armstrong	9/9/67
Bess Armstrong	12/11/53
Louis Armstrong	7/4/00
Neil Armstrong	8/5/30
Anthony Armstrong-Jones	3/7/30
Desi Arnaz	3/2/17
Lucie Arnaz	7/17/51
Desi Arnaz, Jr.	1/19/53
James Arness	5/26/23
Peter Arnett	11/13/34
Benedict Arnold	1/14/1741
Eddy Arnold	5/15/18
Tom Arnold	3/6/59
Boris Aronson	10/15/00
Cliff Arquette	12/28/05
Rosanna Arquette	8/10/59
Richard Arrington	10/19/34
Beatrice Arthur	5/13/26
Jean Arthur	10/17/09
Sholem Asch	11/1/1880

Mary Kay Ash 5/12/15
Peggy Ashcroft 12/22/07
Arthur Ashe 7/10/43
Evelyn Ashford 4/15/57
Nicholas Ashford 5/4/43
Vladimir Ashkenazy 7/6/37
Elizabeth Ashley 8/30/39
Merrill Ashley 12/2/50
Isaac Asimov 1/2/20
Leon Askin 9/18/07
Ed Asner 11/15/29
Les Aspin 7/21/38
Hafez al Assad 10/6/30
Armand Assante 10/4/49
Fred Astaire 5/10/1899
John Astin 3/30/30
Sean Astin 2/25/71
Rick Astley 6/2/66
Mary Astor 5/3/06
William Atherton 7/30/47
Chet Atkins 6/20/24
Christopher Atkins 2/21/61
Brooks Atkinson 11/28/1894
Charles Atlas 10/30/1894
David Attenborough 5/8/26
Richard Attenborough 8/29/23
Stephen Atwater 10/28/66
Lionel Atwill 3/1/1885
Rene Auberjonois 6/1/40
Louis Auchincloss 9/27/17
W.H. Auden 2/21/07
Jean Auel 2/18/36
Mischa Auer 11/17/05
Red Auerbach 9/20/17
Jean-Pierre Aumont 1/5/11
Paul Auster 2/3/47
Jane Austin 12/16/1775
Patti Austin 8/10/48
Pamela Austin 12/20/41
Tracy Austin 12/12/62
Gene Autry 9/29/07
Michael Angelo Avallone 10/27/24
Frankie Avalon 9/18/40
Richard Avedon 5/15/23

Emanuel Ax 6/8/49
George Axelrod 6/9/22
Hoyt Axton 3/25/35
Alan Ayckbourn 4/12/39
Dan Aykroyd 7/1/52
Lew Ayres 12/28/08
Charles Aznavour 5/22/24

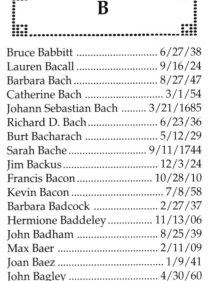

B

Bruce Babbitt 6/27/38
Lauren Bacall 9/16/24
Barbara Bach 8/27/47
Catherine Bach 3/1/54
Johann Sebastian Bach 3/21/1685
Richard D. Bach 6/23/36
Burt Bacharach 5/12/29
Sarah Bache 9/11/1744
Jim Backus 12/3/24
Francis Bacon 10/28/10
Kevin Bacon 7/8/58
Barbara Badcock 2/27/37
Hermione Baddeley 11/13/06
John Badham 8/25/39
Max Baer 2/11/09
Joan Baez 1/9/41
John Bagley 4/30/60
F. Lee Bailey 6/10/33
Pearl Bailey 3/29/18
Philip Bailey 5/8/51
Barbara Bain 9/13/32
Conrad Bain 2/4/23
Harold Bains 3/15/59
Fay Bainter 12/7/1892
Scott Baio 9/22/61
Bill Baird 8/15/04
Al "Bubba" Baker 12/9/56
Anita Baker 1/26/58
Carroll Baker 5/28/35
Diane Baker 2/25/38
Dusty Baker 6/15/49

George Baker 4/1/31	Christiaan Barnard 11/8/22
Howard Baker 11/15/25	Clive Barnes 5/13/27
Janet Baker 8/21/33	JoAnna Barnes 11/15/34
Joe Don Baker 2/12/36	Ross Barnett 1/22/1898
Josephine Baker 6/3/06	P.T. Barnum 7/5/1810
Kenny Baker 9/30/12	Doug Barr 5/1/49
Nicholson Baker 1/7/57	Rona Barrett 10/8/36
Russell Baker 8/14/25	Barbara Barrie 5/23/31
James Baker III 4/28/30	Wendy Barrie 4/18/10
Jim Bakker 1/2/39	Clyde Barrow 3/24/09
George Balanchine 1/9/04	Gene Barry 6/14/22
Alec Baldwin 4/3/58	Marion Barry 3/6/36
James Baldwin 8/2/24	Philip Barry 8/8/23
Roger Baldwin 1/24/1884	Rick Barry 3/28/44
Ina Balin 11/12/37	Sy Barry 2/9/44
Marty Balin 1/30/42	Diana Barrymore 3/3/21
Jerry Ball 12/15/64	Drew Barrymore 2/22/75
Lucille Ball 8/6/11	Ethel Barrymore 8/15/1879
Kaye Ballard 11/20/26	John Barrymore 2/15/1882
Severiano Ballesteras 4/9/57	Lionel Barrymore 4/28/1878
Pierre Balmain 5/18/14	Edgar Paul Barselou 5/31/22
Martin Balsam 11/4/19	Peter Bart 7/24/32
Philip Balsley 8/8/39	John Barth 5/27/30
Anne Bancroft 9/17/31	Donald Barthelme 4/7/31
Tallula Bankhead 1/31/03	Richard Barthelmess 5/9/1895
Carl Banks 8/29/62	Frederic Bartholdi 4/2/1834
Chip Banks 9/18/59	Freddie Bartholomew 3/24/24
Ernie Banks 1/31/31	Hall Bartlett 11/27/29
Vilma Banky 1/9/03	Bela Bartok 5/25/1881
Bob Banner 8/15/21	Eva Bartok 6/18/26
Roger Bannister 3/23/29	Clara Barton 12/25/1821
Theda Bara 7/20/1890	James Barton 11/1/1890
Christine Baranski 5/2/52	Bernard Baruch 8/19/1870
Adrienne Barbeau 6/11/45	Mikhail Baryshnikov 1/27/48
Red Barber 2/17/08	Richard Basehart 8/31/19
Samuel Barber 3/9/10	Count Basie 8/21/04
Brigitte Bardot 9/28/34	Kim Basinger 12/8/53
Bobby Bare 4/7/35	Saul Bass 5/8/20
Daniel Barenboim 11/15/42	Shirley Bassey 1/8/37
Bob Barker 12/12/23	Jason Bateman 1/14/69
Clive Barker 10/5/52	Justine Bateman 2/19/66
Lex Barker 5/8/19	Alan Bates 2/17/34
Ellen Barkin 4/16/55	Kathy Bates 6/28/48
Charles Barkley 2/20/63	Kathleen Battle 8/13/48

Alan Baxter	11/19/08
Anne Baxter	5/7/23
Keith Baxter	4/29/35
Meredith Baxter	6/21/47
Warner Baxter	3/29/1891
Birch Bayh	1/22/28
Don Baylor	6/28/49
Elgin Baylor	9/16/34
Stephanie Beacham	2/28/47
John Beal	8/13/09
Jennifer Beals	12/19/63
Bob Beamon	8/29/46
Alan Bean	3/15/32
Andy Bean	3/13/53
Orson Bean	7/22/28
Aubrey Beardsley	8/21/1872
Bobby Beathard	1/24/37
Ann Beattie	9/8/47
Cecil Beaton	1/14/04
Ned Beatty	7/6/37
Robert Beatty	10/19/09
Warren Beatty	3/30/37
Louise Beavers	3/8/02
Jeff Beck	6/24/44
Boris Becker	11/22/67
Samuel Beckett	4/13/06
Bonnie Bedelia	3/25/48
Brian Bedford	2/16/35
Steve Bedrosian	12/6/57
Sir Thomas Beecham	4/29/1879
Geoffrey Beene	8/30/27
Noah Beery	1/7/1884
Noah Beery, Jr.	1/10/16
Wallace Beery	4/1/1886
Ludwig van Beethoven	12/16/1770
Menachem Begin	8/16/13
Ed Begley	3/25/01
Ed Begley, Jr.	9/16/49
Brendan Behan	2/9/23
Bix Beiderbecke	3/10/03
Barbara Bel-Geddes	10/31/22
Harry Belafonte	3/1/27
Shari Belafonte	9/22/54
Albert Bell	8/25/66
Alexander Graham Bell	3/3/1847
Cool Papa Bell	5/17/03
Rex Bell	10/16/05
Madge Bellamy	6/30/00
Ralph Bellamy	6/17/04
Melvin Belli	7/29/07
Vincenzo Bellini	11/3/1801
Saul Bellow	6/10/15
Louie Bellson	7/6/24
Jean-Paul Belmondo	4/9/33
Jim Belush	6/15/54
John Belush	1/24/49
David Ben-Gurion	10/16/1886
Pat Benatar	1/10/52
Johnny Bench	12/7/47
Nathaniel Benchley	11/13/15
Peter Benchley	5/8/40
Robert Benchley	9/15/1889
Gary Bender	9/1/40
William Bendix	1/4/06
Ted Benecke	2/12/14
Dirk Benedict	3/1/44
Stephen Vincent Benet	7/22/1898
Annette Bening	5/29/58
Richard Benjamin	5/22/38
Constance Bennett	10/22/05
Harve Bennett	8/17/30
Jill Bennett	12/24/31
Joan Bennett	2/27/10
Michael Bennett	4/8/43
Tony Bennett	8/3/26
William Bennett	7/31/43
Jack Benny	2/14/1894
George Benson	3/22/43
Robby Benson	1/21/57
Barbi Benton	1/28/50
Thomas Hart Benton	4/15/1889
Lloyd Bentsen	2/11/21
Tom Berenger	5/31/50
Marisa Berenson	2/15/48
Bruce Beresford	8/16/40
Gertrude Berg	10/3/1899
Candice Bergen	5/9/46
Edgar Bergen	2/16/03

Polly Bergen	7/14/30	Joseph Biden	11/20/42
Helmut Berger	5/29/44	Owen Bieber	12/28/29
Nicole Berger	6/12/35	Bijan	4/4/40
Jacques Bergerac	5/26/27	Theodore Bikel	5/2/24
Ingmar Bergman	7/14/18	Tony Bill	8/23/40
Ingrid Bergman	8/29/16	Barbara Billingsley	12/22/22
Carlo Bergonzi	7/13/24	Billy the Kid	11/23/1859
Busby Berkeley	11/29/1895	Dave Bing	11/24/43
David Berkowitz	6/1/53	Matt Bionde	10/8/65
Milton Berle	7/12/08	Larry Bird	12/7/56
Irving Berlin	5/11/1888	Stephen Birmingham	5/28/31
Roger Stuart Berlind	6/27/30	David Birney	4/23/40
Warren Berlinger	8/31/37	Joey Bishop	2/3/18
Hector Berlioz	12/11/1803	Julie Bishop	8/30/14
Pandro Berman	3/28/05	Jacqueline Bisset	9/13/44
Shelly Berman	2/3/26	Bill Bixby	1/22/34
Herschel Bernardi	10/30/23	George Bizet	10/25/1838
Sandra Bernhard	6/6/55	Clint Black	2/4/62
Sarah Bernhardt	10/23/1844	Karen Black	7/1/42
Gian Lorenzo Bernini	12/7/1598	Honor Blackman	8/22/29
Corbin Bernsen	9/7/54	Sidney Blackmer	7/13/1896
Carl Bernstein	2/14/44	Harry Blackmun	11/12/08
Elmer Bernstein	4/4/22	Harry Blackstone	6/30/34
Leonard Bernstein	8/25/18	Bennie Blades	9/3/66
Yoga Berra	5/12/25	Ruben Blades	7/16/48
Chuck Berry	1/15/26	Nell Walden Blaine	7/10/22
Halle Berry	8/14/68	Vivian Blaine	11/21/24
Jan Berry	4/3/43	Betsy Blair	12/11/23
Ken Berry	11/3/33	Bonnie Blair	3/18/64
Mary Frances Berry	2/17/38	Janet Blair	4/23/21
Raymond Berry	2/27/33	Linda Blair	1/22/59
John Berryman	10/25/14	Amanda Blake	2/20/31
Valerie Bertinelli	4/23/60	Jeff Blake	12/4/70
Bernardo Bertolucci	3/16/40	William Blake	11/28/1757
Bruno Bettelheim	8/28/03	Susan Blakely	9/7/48
Jerome Bettis	2/16/72	Eubie Blakes	2/7/1883
Dicky Betts	12/12/43	Robert Blakes	9/18/33
Carl Betz	3/9/20	Art Blakey	10/11/19
Turhan Bey	3/30/20	Jane Blalock	9/19/45
Richard Beymer	2/21/39	Mel Blanc	5/30/08
Mayim Bialik	12/12/75	Doc Blanchard	12/11/24
Leon Bibb	2/7/22	Mari Blanchard	4/13/27
Bernie Bickerstaff	11/2/43	Bobby "Blue" Bland	1/27/30
Charles Bickford	1/1/1889	George Blanda	9/17/27

Clara Blandick 6/4/1880	Erma Bombeck 2/21/27
Sally Blane 7/11/10	Napoleon Bonaparte 8/15/1769
Bill Blass 6/22/22	Julian Bond 1/14/40
William Peter Blatty 1/7/28	Ward Bond 4/9/04
Mookie Blaylock 3/20/67	Beulah Bondi 5/3/1892
Drew Bledsoe 2/14/72	Barry Bonds 7/24/64
Jules Bledsoe 12/29/1898	Bobby Bonds 3/15/46
Tempest Bledsoe 8/1/73	Gary U.S. Bonds 6/6/39
Rocky Bleier 3/5/46	Peter Bonerz 8/6/38
Mary J. Blige 1/11/71	Lisa Bonet 11/16/67
William Bligh 9/8/1754	Bobby Bonilla 2/23/63
Joan Blondell 8/30/12	David Bonior 6/6/45
Linda Bloodworth-Thomason. 4/15/47	Yelena Bonner 2/15/23
Clair Bloom 2/15/31	Bono 5/10/60
Mike Bloomfield 7/28/43	Chastity Bono 3/4/69
Betsy Bloomingdale 8/2/26	Sonny Bono 2/16/40
Monte Blue 1/11/1890	Karla Bonoff 12/27/52
Vida Blue 7/28/49	Joseph Bonsall 5/18/48
Guion Bluford 11/22/42	Jon Bon Jovi 3/2/61
Judy Blume 2/12/38	Sorrell Booke.................... 1/4/30
Nellie Bly 5/5/1867	Daniel Boone 11/2/1734
Ann Blyth 8/16/28	Debbie Boone 9/22/56
Umberto Boccioni 10/19/1882	Pat Boone 6/1/34
Steve Bochco 12/16/43	Richard Boone 6/18/17
Hart Bochner 10/3/56	John Boorman 1/18/33
Lloyd Bochner 7/29/24	Elayne Boosler 8/18/52
Paul Bocuse..................... 2/11/26	John Wilkes Booth 5/10/1838
Dirk Bogarde 3/28/21	Shirley Booth 8/30/07
Humphrey Bogart 12/25/1899	Gail Borden 11/9/1801
Paul Bogart 11/21/19	Lizzie Borden.................... 7/19/1860
Peter Bogdonovich 7/30/39	David Boren 4/21/41
Wade Boggs 6/15/58	Bjorn Borg 6/6/56
Suzy Bogguss.................... 12/30/56	Victor Borge 1/3/09
Eric Bogosian 4/24/53	Jorge Luis Borges 8/24/1899
Muggsy Bogues.................... 1/9/65	Gutzon Borglum 3/25/1867
Karl Bohn 8/28/1894	Ernest Borgnine.................... 1/24/17
Niels Bohr 10/7/1895	Frank Borman 3/14/28
Brian Boitano 10/22/63	Alexander Borodin 11/12/1833
Derek Bok..................... 3/22/30	Philip Michael Bosco 9/26/30
Manute Bol 10/16/62	Tom Bosley 10/1/27
Giovanni Boldini 12/31/1842	Barbara Bosson 11/1/39
Ray Bolger 1/10/04	Mike Bossy 1/22/57
Robert Bolt 8/15/24	Barry Bostwick 2/24/45
Michael Bolton 2/26/53	James Boswell.................... 10/29/1740

Brain Bosworth 3/9/65	Cliff Branch 8/1/48
Fernando Botero 4/19/32	Neville Brand 8/13/21
P.W. Botha 1/12/16	Klaus Marie Brandauer 6/22/44
Joseph Bottoms 4/22/54	Louis Brandeis 11/13/1856
Timothy Bottoms 8/30/51	Marlon Brando 4/3/24
Lou Boudreau 7/17/17	Willy Brandt 12/18/13
Muggsy Bougues 1/9/65	Laura Branigan 7/3/57
Pierre Boulez 3/26/25	Richard Branson 7/18/50
Margaret Bourke-White 6/14/04	Keefe Brasselle 2/7/23
Jim Bouton 3/8/39	Toni Braxton 10/7/67
Boutro Boutros-Ghali 11/14/22	T. Berry Brazelton 5/10/18
Clara Bow 8/25/05	Rossano Brazzi 9/18/16
Larry Bowa 12/6/45	Julian Bream 7/15/33
Riddick Bowe 8/10/67	Bertolt Brecht 2/10/1898
Major Bowes 6/14/1874	Craig Breedlove 3/23/37
David Bowie 1/8/47	Jacques Brel 4/8/29
Sam Bowie 3/17/61	Eileen Brennan 9/3/37
Lee Bowman 12/28/14	Walter Brennan 7/25/1894
Scotty Bowman 9/18/33	William Brennan, Jr. 4/25/06
Barbara Boxer 11/11/40	David Brenner 2/4/45
Bruce Boxleitner 5/12/51	George Brent 3/15/04
Bill Boyd 6/5/1898	Jimmy Breslin 10/17/30
Stephen Boyd 7/4/28	George Brett 5/15/53
William Boyd 6/5/1898	Jeremy Brett 11/3/35
Charles Boyer 8/28/1899	Theresa Brewer 5/7/31
Pappy Boyington 12/4/06	Stephen Breyer 8/15/38
John Boylan 3/21/41	Leonid Brezhnev 12/19/06
Peter Boyle 10/18/35	David Brian 8/5/14
Eddie Bracken 2/7/20	Fanny Brice 10/29/1891
Charles Brackett 11/26/1892	Jack Brickhouse 1/24/16
Ray Bradbury 8/22/20	Beau Bridges 12/9/41
Ben Bradlee 8/26/21	Jeff Bridges 12/4/49
Bill Bradley 7/28/43	Lloyd Bridges 1/15/13
Ed Bradley 6/22/41	Todd Bridges 5/27/65
Gen. Omar Bradley 2/12/1893	Wilford Brimley 9/27/34
Pat Bradley 3/24/51	Christie Brinkley 2/2/53
Shawn Bradley 3/22/72	David Brinkley 7/10/20
Tom Bradley 12/29/17	Valerie Brisco-Hooks 7/6/60
Terry Bradshaw 9/2/48	Danielle Brisebois 6/28/69
James Brady 8/29/40	May Britt 3/22/33
Nicholas Brady 4/11/30	Morgan Brittany 12/5/51
Scott Brady 9/13/24	Barbara Britton 9/26/19
Louis Braille 1/4/1809	Albert "Cubby" Broccoli 4/5/09
Kenneth Branagh 12/10/60	Lou Brock 6/18/39

David Broder 9/11/29	Vanessa Brown 3/24/28
Matthew Broderick 3/21/62	Dik Browne 8/11/18
John Brodie 8/14/35	Jackson Browne 10/9/50
Steve Brodie 11/25/19	Roscoe Lee Browne 5/2/25
Tom Brokaw 2/6/40	John Browning 5/23/33
James Brolin 7/18/41	John Moses Browning 1/21/1854
Edgan Bronfman 6/20/29	Robert Browning 5/7/1812
Jacob Bronowski 1/18/08	Tod Browning 7/12/1884
Charles Bronson 11/3/22	Susan Brownmiller 2/15/35
Charlotte Bronte 4/21/1816	David Brubeck 12/6/20
Emily Bronte 7/30/1818	Carol Bruce 11/15/19
Clive Brook 6/1/1887	Lenny Bruce 10/13/25
Peter Brook 3/21/25	Nigel Bruce 9/4/1895
Edward Brooke 10/26/19	Virginia Bruce 9/29/10
Hillary Brooke 9/8/16	William Jennings Bryan 3/19/1860
Albert Brooks 7/22/47	Anita Bryant 3/25/40
Donald Brooks 1/10/28	Mark Bryan 5/6/67
Foster Brooks 5/11/12	Paul "Bear" Bryant 9/11/13
Garth Brooks 2/7/62	William Cullen Bryant 11/2/1794
Geraldine Brooks 10/29/25	Yul Brynner 7/12/20
Gwendolyn Brooks 6/7/17	Peabo Bryson 4/13/51
James L. Brooks 5/9/40	Zbigniew Brzezinski 3/28/28
Louise Brooks 11/14/06	Edgar Buchanan 3/21/03
Mel Brooks 6/28/28	Edgar Buchanan 3/20/03
Richard Brooks 5/18/12	Ian Buchanan 6/16/55
Kevin Brophy 9/11/53	Patrick Buchanan 11/2/38
Pierce Brosnan 5/16/53	Roy Buchanan 9/23/39
Dr. Joyce Brothers 10/20/28	Horst Buchholz 12/4/33
Heywood Hale Broun 3/10/18	Art Buchwald 10/20/25
Arthur Brown 6/24/44	Frank Buck 3/17/1884
Bobby Brown 2/4/69	Peal Buck 6/26/1892
David Brown 7/28/16	Lindsey Buckingham 10/3/49
Dee Brown 11/29/68	Betty Buckley 7/3/47
Gate Brown 3/2/39	William F. Buckley, Jr. 11/24/25
Helen Gurley Brown 2/18/22	Bill Buckner 12/14/49
James Brown 5/3/36	Don Budge 6/13/15
Jerry Brown 4/7/38	Jimmy Buffett 12/25/46
Jim Brown 2/17/36	Genevieve Bujold 7/1/42
John Brown 5/9/1800	Fernando Bujones 3/9/55
Larry Brown 9/14/40	Ed Bullins 7/25/35
Les Brown 3/14/12	Grace Bumbry 1/4/37
Paul Brown 9/7/08	Ralph Bunche 8/7/04
Ron Brown 8/1/41	McGeorge Bundy 3/30/19
Tony Brown 4/11/33	Bettina Bunge 6/13/63

Jim Bunning 10/23/31
John Bunny 9/21/1863
Mary Bunting 7/10/10
Luis Bunuel 2/22/00
Nick Buoniconti 12/15/40
Victor Buono 2/3/38
Warren Burger 9/17/07
Anthony Burgess 2/15/17
Gary Burghoff 5/24/43
Billie Burke 8/7/1886
Chris Burke 8/26/65
Delta Burke 7/30/56
Paul Burke 7/21/26
Joycelyn Bell Burnell 7/15/43
Carol Burnett 4/26/36
Smiley Burnette 3/18/11
Arthur Burns 4/27/04
George Burns 1/20/1896
James MacGregor Burns 8/3/18
Jerry Burns 1/24/27
Ken Burns 7/29/53
Peter Burns 8/15/59
Raymond Burr 5/21/17
Edgar Rice Burroughs 9/1/1875
Abe Burrows 12/18/10
James Burrows 12/30/40
William Burrows 2/5/14
Ellen Burstyn 12/7/32
LeVar Burton 2/16/57
Richard Burton 11/10/25
Leo Buscaglia 3/31/25
August Busch, Jr. 3/28/1899
Gary Busey 6/29/44
Timothy Busfield 6/12/57
Barbara Bush 6/8/25
George Bush 6/12/24
Kate Bush 7/30/58
Joey Bushin 11/7/16
Francis X. Bushman 1/10/1883
Dick Butkus 12/9/42
Jerry Butler 12/8/39
Dick Button 7/18/29
Red Button 2/5/19
Ruth Buzzi 7/24/36

Keith Byars 10/14/63
Spring Byington 10/17/1893
Charles Byrd 9/16/25
Robert Byrd 11/20/17
David Byrne 5/14/52
Jane Byrne 5/24/34
Edd Byrnes 7/30/33

C

James Caan 3/26/39
Montserrat Caballe 4/12/33
Bruce Cabot 4/20/04
Sebastian Cabot 7/6/18
Michael Cacoyannis 6/11/22
Greg Caderet 2/27/62
Julius Caesar 7/12/100BC
Shirley Caesar 10/13/38
Sid Caesar 9/8/22
John Cage 9/5/12
Nicolas Cage 1/7/64
James Cagney 7/17/1899
Sammy Cahn 6/18/13
James M. Cain 7/1/1892
Michael Caine 3/14/33
Mark Calcavecchin 6/6/60
Alexander Calder 7/22/1898
Erskine Caldwell 12/17/03
Sarah Caldwell 3/6/24
Taylor Caldwell 9/7/00
Zoe Caldwell 9/14/33
Louis Calhern 2/19/1895
John Caldwell Calhoun 3/18/1782
Rory Calhoun 8/8/23
Michael Callan 11/22/35
Maria Callas 12/2/23
Cab Calloway 12/25/07
Corinne Calvet 4/30/25
Hector Camacho 5/24/62
Godfrey Cambridge 2/26/33
Julia M. Cameron 6/11/1815

Kirk Cameron	10/12/70
Roy Cameron	12/7/12
Joseph Camp	4/20/39
Joseph Campanella	11/21/27
Roy Campanella	11/19/21
Bert Campaneris	3/9/42
Ben Nighthorse Campbell	4/13/33
Earl Campbell	3/29/55
Glen Campbell	4/22/38
Naomi Campbell	5/22/70
Tisha Campbell	10/13/70
Albert Camus	11/7/13
John Candy	10/31/50
Milton Caniff	2/28/07
Stephen Cannell	2/5/41
Dyan Cannon	1/4/39
Judy Canova	11/20/16
Jose Canseco	7/2/64
Cantinflas	8/12/11
Eddie Cantor	1/31/1892
Lana Cantrell	8/7/43
Jim Capaldi	8/24/44
Al Capone	1/17/1899
Truman Capote	9/30/24
Al Capp	9/28/09
John Cappellett	8/9/52
Frank Capra	5/18/1897
Jennifer Capriati	3/29/76
Capucine	1/6/35
Philip Caputo	6/10/41
Irene Cara	3/18/59
Roger Caras	5/24/28
Harry Caray	3/1/19
Pierre Cardin	7/7/22
Claudia Cardinale	4/15/38
Franco Carelli	4/8/23
Rod Carew	10/1/45
MacDonald Carey	3/15/14
Harry Carey, Jr.	5/16/21
Mariah Carey	3/27/70
Ron Carey	12/11/35
Len Carion	9/30/39
George Carlin	5/12/37
Belinda Carlisle	8/17/58

Kitty Carlisle	9/3/15
King Juan Carlos	1/5/38
Richard Carlson	4/29/12
Steve Carlton	12/22/44
Hoagy Carmichael	11/22/1899
Stokely Carmichael	6/29/41
Dale Carnegie	11/24/1888
Primo Carnera	10/26/06
Kim Carnes	7/20/46
Art Carney	11/4/18
Morris Carnovsky	9/5/1897
Prinesss Caroline	1/23/57
Leslie Caron	7/1/31
Carleton Carpenter	7/10/26
John H. Carpenter	1/16/48
Karen Carpenter	3/2/50
Mary-Chapin Carpenter	2/21/58
Richard Carpenter	10/15/46
Scott Carpenter	5/1/25
Allen Carr	5/27/41
Vikki Carr	7/19/41
David Carradine	12/8/36
John Carradine	2/5/06
Keith Carradine	8/8/49
Robert Carradine	3/24/54
Jose Carreras	12/5/46
Jim Carrey	1/17/62
Leo Carrillo	8/6/1880
Pat Carrol	5/5/27
Diahann Carroll	7/17/35
John Carroll	7/17/05
Leo G. Carroll	10/18/1892
Lewis Carroll	1/27/1832
Marcia Carsey	11/21/44
Jack Carson	10/27/10
Johnny Carson	10/23/25
Kit Carson	12/24/1809
Amy Carter	10/19/67
Anthony Carter	9/17/60
Betty Carter	5/16/27
Billy Carter	3/29/37
Cris Carter	11/25/65
Don Carter	7/29/26
Elliot Carter	12/11/08

14

Gary Carter 4/8/54	Phoebe Cates 7/16/63
Jack Carter 6/25/23	Willa Cather 12/7/1873
James E. Carter 12/15/24	Catherine the Great 5/2/1729
Jimmy Carter 10/1/24	Bruce Catton 10/9/1899
Joe Carter 3/7/60	Joan Caulfield 6/1/22
Ki-Jana Carter 9/12/73	Maxwell Caufield 11/23/59
Lillian Carter 8/15/1898	Macauley Caulkin 8/20/80
Lynda Carter 7/24/51	Steve Cauthen 5/1/60
Nell Carter 9/13/48	Carmen Cavallaro 5/6/13
Rosalynn Carter 8/18/27	Dick Cavett 11/19/36
Tracy Carter 2/16/40	Benvenuto Cellini 11/1/1500
June Carter-Cash 6/23/29	Kathy Cennon 8/22/42
Hodding Carter III 4/7/35	Orlando Cepeda 9/17/37
Barbara Cartland 7/9/01	Eugene A. Cernan 3/14/34
Bill Cartwright 7/30/57	Miguel de Cervantes 9/29/1547
David Caruso 1/17/56	Ron Cey 2/15/48
Enrico Caruso 2/25/1873	Claude Chabrol 6/24/30
George Washington Carver... 1/4/1859	Florence Chadwick 11/9/18
Dana Carvey 4/2/55	Roger B. Chaffee 2/15/35
James Carville 10/25/44	Suzy Chaffee 11/29/46
Pablo Casals 12/29/1876	Marc Chagall 7/7/1887
Rosemary Casals 9/16/48	George Chakiris 9/16/34
William Casey 3/13/13	Violeta Chamarro 10/18/29
Johnny Cash 2/26/32	Neville Chamberlain 3/18/1869
Norm Cash 10/11/34	Richard Chamberlain 3/31/35
Pat Cash 5/27/65	Wilt Chamberlain 8/21/36
Rosanne Cash 5/24/55	Tom Chambers 6/21/59
Stefano Casiraghi 9/8/60	Marge Champion 9/2/23
Billy Casper 6/24/31	John Chancellor 7/14/27
Peggy Cass 5/21/25	Happy Chandler 7/14/1898
Mary Cassatt 5/22/1844	Jeff Chandler 12/15/18
John Cassavetes 12/9/29	Coco Chanel 8/19/1882
Butch Cassidy 4/6/1867	Don Chaney 3/22/46
David Cassidy 4/12/50	Lon Chaney 4/1/1883
Jack Cassidy 3/5/27	Lon Chaney, Jr. 2/10/05
Shaun Cassidy 9/27/58	Michael Chang 2/22/72
Oleg Cassini 4/11/13	Carol Channing 1/31/23
Richard Castellano 9/4/34	Stockard Channing 2/13/44
Irene Castle 4/7/1893	Harry Chapin 12/7/42
Vernon Castle 5/2/1887	Charlie Chaplin 4/16/1889
William Castle 4/24/14	Geraldine Chaplin 7/31/44
Fidel Castro 8/13/27	Mark David Chapman 5/10/55
Raul Castro 6/3/31	Jean Baptise Chardin 11/2/1699
Gilbert Cates 6/6/34	Cyd Charisse 3/8/23

Charlemagne .... 4/2/742 AD	Henry Cisneros 6/11/47
Ezzard Charles 7/7/21	Liz Claiborne 3/31/29
Prince Charles 11/14/48	Rene Clair 11/11/1898
Ray Charles 9/23/30	Ina Claire 10/15/1895
Charo 1/15/51	Eric Clapton 3/30/45
Barrie Chase 10/20/34	Dane Clark 2/18/13
Chevy Chase 10/8/43	Dick Clark 11/30/29
Lucia Chase 3/24/07	Dave Clark 12/15/42
Silvia Chase 2/23/38	Fred Clark 3/9/14
Cesar Chavez 3/31/27	Gary Clark 5/1/62
Benjamin Chavis 1/22/48	Gen. Mark Clark 5/1/1896
Paddy Chayefsky 1/29/23	Joe Clark 5/7/39
Calbert Cheaney 7/17/71	Kenneth B. Clark 7/24/14
Chubby Checker 10/3/41	Marcia Clark 8/31/53
Cheech (Richard Martin) 7/13/46	Mary Higgins Clark 12/24/31
Maurice Cheeks 9/8/56	Petula Clark 11/15/32
John Cheever 5/27/12	Ramsey Clark 12/18/27
Richard Cheney 1/30/41	Roy Clark 4/15/33
Cher 5/20/46	Susan Clark 3/8/44
Charles Chesnutt 6/20/1858	Wil Clark 3/13/64
Mark Chestnutt 9/6/63	Arthur Clarke 12/16/17
Maurice Chevalier 9/12/1888	Mae Clarke 8/16/07
Tim Cheveldae 2/15/68	Robert Clary 3/1/26
Julia Child 8/15/12	James Clavell 10/10/24
Lawton Chiles 4/3/30	Jill Clayburgh 4/30/44
Thomas Chippendale 6/5/1718	Adam Clayton 3/13/60
Shirley Chisholm 11/30/24	Mark Clayton 4/8/61
Marvin Chomsky 5/23/29	Eldridge Cleaver 8/31/35
Tommy Chong 5/24/38	John Cleese 10/27/39
Frederic Chopin 2/22/1810	Roger Clemens 8/4/62
Jesus Christ .... 12/25/04 BC	Roberto Clemente 8/18/34
Linda Christian 11/13/23	Clarence Clemons 1/11/42
Agatha Christie 9/15/1890	Grover Cleveland 3/18/1837
Julie Christie 4/14/40	Van Cliburn 7/12/34
Virginia Field Christine 3/5/20	Montgomery Cliff 10/17/20
Christo 6/13/35	Clark Clifford 12/25/06
Warren Christopher 10/27/25	Patsy Cline 9/8/32
Marian Christy 11/9/32	Bill Clinton 8/19/46
Connie Chung 8/20/46	Chelsea Clinton 2/27/80
Frank Church 7/25/24	George Clinton 7/22/41
Sandra Church 1/13/43	Hillary Rodham Clinton 10/26/47
Sarah Churchill 10/7/14	George Clooney 5/6/61
Winston Churchill 11/30/1874	Rosemary Clooney 5/23/28
Diane Cilento 10/5/33	Glenn Close 3/19/47

16

Lee J. Cobb	12/8/11
Ty Cobb	12/18/1893
Charles Coburn	6/19/1865
James Coburn	8/31/28
Imogene Coca	11/18/08
Barbara Ann Cochran	1/4/51
Johnnie Cochran, Jr	10/2/37
Steve Cochran	5/25/17
Thad Cochran	12/7/37
Joe Cocker	5/20/44
James Coco	3/21/29
Jean Cocteau	7/5/1889
Buffalo Bill Cody	2/26/1846
Iron Eyes Cody	4/3/15
David Allen Coe	9/6/39
Sebastian Coe	9/29/56
Tony Coelho	6/15/42
George M. Cohan	7/3/1878
William Cohen	8/28/40
Rocky Colavito	8/10/33
Claudette Colbert	9/13/05
Dennis Cole	7/18/43
Natalie Cole	2/6/49
Nat "King" Cole	3/17/19
Cy Coleman	6/14/29
Dabney Coleman	1/3/32
Derrick Coleman	6/21/67
Gary Coleman	2/8/68
Jack Coleman	2/21/58
Ornette Coleman	3/19/30
Ronald Coleman	2/9/1891
Samuel Taylor Coleridge	8/15/1875
Charles Collingwood	6/4/17
Dorothy Collins	11/18/26
Jackie Collins	10/4/41
Joan Collins	5/23/33
Judy Collins	5/1/39
Michael Collins	7/20/69
Pauline Collins	9/3/40
Phil Collins	1/30/51
Stephen Collins	10/1/47
Cris Collinsworth	1/27/59
Bud Collyer	6/18/08
Johnny Colt	5/1/68

Jessi Colter	5/25/47
Alice Coltrane	8/27/37
John Coltrane	9/23/26
Russ Columbo	1/4/08
Nadia Comaneci	11/12/61
Betty Comden	5/3/15
Charles Comiskey	8/15/1859
Henry Steel Commager	10/25/02
Perry Como	5/18/12
Ann Compton	1/29/47
Jeff Conaway	10/5/50
Richard Condon	3/18/15
David Cone	1/2/63
Confucius	8/27/550 BC
John Conlee	8/11/46
John Connally	2/27/17
Marc Connelly	12/13/1890
Sean Connery	8/25/30
Harry Connick, Jr.	9/11/67
Chuck Connors	4/10/21
Jimmy Connors	9/2/52
Mike Connors	8/15/21
Joseph Conrad	12/3/1857
Paul F. Conrad	6/27/24
Robert Conrad	3/1/35
William Conrad	9/27/20
Charles Conrad, Jr.	6/2/30
Hans Conreid	4/1/15
Pat Conroy	10/26/45
Richard Conte	3/24/14
Bill Conti	4/13/42
Tom Conti	11/22/41
Bert Convy	7/23/34
Kevin Conway	5/29/42
Tim Conway	12/15/33
John Conyers, Jr.	5/16/29
Ry Cooder	3/15/47
Jackie Coogan	10/24/14
Barbara Cook	10/25/27
Jeff Cook	8/27/49
Peter Cook	11/17/37
Elisha Cook, Jr.	12/26/06
Alistair Cooke	11/20/08
Sam Cooke	1/22/31

Terence Cardinal Cooke 3/1/21
Dr. Denton Cooley 8/22/20
Calvin Coolidge 7/4/1872
Rita Coolidge 5/1/45
Gerry Cooney 8/24/56
Joan Ganz Cooney 11/30/29
Alice Cooper 2/4/48
Gary Cooper 5/7/01
Hal Cooper 2/23/23
Jackie Cooper 9/15/22
James Fenimore Cooper 9/15/1789
L. Gordon Cooper 3/6/27
Michael Cooper 4/15/56
Joseph Coors 11/12/17
Aaron Copland 11/14/00
Teri Copley 5/10/61
David Copperfield 9/16/56
Francis Coppola 4/7/39
Ellen Corby 6/3/13
Alex Cord 8/3/31
Angel Cordero 11/8/42
Chick Corea 6/12/41
Franco Corelli 4/8/23
Jeff Corey.................................. 8/10/14
Wendell Corey 3/20/14
Roger Corman 4/5/26
Don Cornelius 9/27/36
Don Cornell 4/21/19
Katherine Cornell 2/16/1898
Correggio 8/30/1494
Bud Cort 3/29/51
Ricardo Cortez...................... 9/19/1899
Norman Corwin 5/3/10
Dave Corzine 4/25/56
Bill Cosby 7/12/37
Howard Cosell 3/25/20
Bob Costas 3/22/52
Dolores Costello 9/17/05
Elvis Costello 8/25/55
Lou Costello 3/6/08
Kevin Costner 1/18/55
Joseph Cotton 5/15/05
Dave Coulier............................. 9/21/59
George Coulouris 10/1/03

Fred Couples 10/3/59
Gustava Courbet 6/10/1819
Katie Couric 1/7/57
Jim Courier 8/17/70
Margaret Smith Court 7/16/42
Tom Courtenay 2/25/37
Norman Cousins 6/24/15
Jacques Cousteau 6/11/10
Bob Cousy 8/9/28
Franklin Cover 11/20/28
Jerome Cowan 10/6/1897
Noel Coward 12/16/1899
Dave Cowens........................... 10/25/48
Archibald Cox 5/17/12
Courteney Cox 6/15/64
Wally Cox................................. 12/6/24
Steve Coy 3/15/62
Buster Crabbe 2/17/06
Larry "Buster" Crabbe 2/6/08
Roger Craig 7/10/60
Roger Craig (Baseball).............. 2/17/30
Jeanne Crain 5/25/25
Bob Crane 7/13/28
Hart Crane 7/21/1899
Stephen Crane 11/1/1871
Alan Cranston 6/19/14
Broderick Crawford 12/9/11
Cindy Crawford 2/20/66
Joan Crawford 3/23/08
Michael Crawford 1/19/42
Robert Cray 8/1/53
Richard Crenna 11/30/27
Ben Crenshaw 1/11/52
Laura Hope Crews 12/12/1879
Michael Crichton 10/23/42
Francis Crick 6/8/16
Donald Crisp 7/27/1880
Quentin Crisp 12/25/08
Judith Crist............................... 5/22/22
Jim Croce 1/10/43
David Crockett 8/17/1786
David Cronberg 5/15/43
Walter Cronkite :...................... 11/4/16
Hume Cronyn 7/18/11

Bing Crosby 5/2/04
David Crosby 8/14/41
Gary Crosby 6/27/33
Joan Carew Crosby 2/14/34
Kathryn Crosby 11/25/33
Mary Crosby 9/14/59
Norm Crosby 9/15/27
Ben Cross 12/16/47
Christopher Cross 5/3/51
Irv Cross 7/27/39
Scatman Crothers 5/23/10
Andreae Crouch 7/1/42
Lindsay Crouse 5/12/48
Cameron Crowe 7/13/57
William Crowe 1/2/25
Rodney Crowell 8/7/50
Patricia Crowley 9/17/38
Bosley Crowther 7/13/05
Tom Cruise 7/3/62
Denny Crum 3/2/37
Robert Crumb 8/30/43
Harold Cruse 3/8/16
Billy Crystal 3/14/47
Larry Csonka 12/25/46
Xavier Cugat 1/1/00
George Cukor 7/7/1899
Macaulay Culkin 8/26/80
Bill Cullen 2/18/20
John Cullum 3/2/30
Robert Culp 8/16/30
Hugh Culverhouse 2/20/19
Constance Cummings 5/15/10
E.E. Cummings 10/14/1894
Robert Cummings 6/9/10
Terry Cummings 3/15/61
Billy Cunningham 6/3/43
Merce Cunningham 4/16/19
Randall Cunningham 3/27/63
Sam Cunningham 8/15/50
Mario Cuomo 6/15/32
Eve Curie 12/6/04
Madame Curie 11/7/1867
John Curry 9/9/49
Tim Curry 4/19/46

Jane Curtin 9/6/47
Phyllis Curtin 12/3/27
Jamie Lee Curtis 11/22/58
King Curtis 3/7/34
Tony Curtis 6/3/25
Michael Curtiz 12/24/1898
Joan Cusack 10/11/62
John Cusack 6/28/66
Sinead Cusack 2/18/48
Peter Cushing 5/26/13
George Armstrong Custer ... 12/5/1839
Billy Ray Cyrus 8/25/61

D

Alfonse D'Amato 8/1/37
Jacques D'Amboise 7/28/34
Beverly D'Angelo 11/15/53
Terence Trent D'Arby 3/15/62
Fifi D'Orsay 4/16/04
Willem Dafoe 7/22/55
Arlene Dahl 8/11/27
Roald Dahl 9/13/16
Dan Dailey 12/14/15
Irene Dailey 9/12/20
Janet Dailey 5/21/44
Quintin Dailey 1/22/61
The Dalai Lama 7/6/35
Jim Dale 8/15/35
Cass Daley 7/17/15
Richard Daley 4/24/42
Richard J. Daley 5/15/02
Salvador Dali 5/11/04
Marcell Dalio 7/17/00
Joe Dallesando 12/31/48
Timothy Dalton 3/21/46
Roger Daltrey 3/1/44
Chuck Daly 7/20/33
James Daly 10/23/18
Timothy Daly 3/1/56
Tyne Daly 2/21/44

Giorgio deChirico 7/10/1880	Sandy Dennis 4/27/37
Mary Decker 8/4/58	John Densmore 12/1/44
Dennis DeConcini 5/8/37	Bucky Dent 11/25/51
Fred DeCordova 10/27/10	Richard Dent 12/13/60
Midge Decter 7/25/27	Bob Denver 1/9/35
Ruby Dee 10/27/24	John Denver 12/31/43
Sandra Dee 4/23/42	Brian Depalma 9/11/40
Ada Deer 8/7/35	Gerard Depardieu 12/27/48
John Deere 2/7/1804	Johnny Depp 6/9/63
Morris S. Dees, Jr. 12/16/36	Bo Derek 11/20/56
Frank Deford 12/16/38	John Derek 8/12/26
Don DeFore 8/25/26	Bruce Dern 6/4/36
Edgar Degas 7/19/1834	Delion DeShields 1/15/69
Charles DeGaulle 11/22/1890	Vittorio DeSica 7/7/02
Ellen DeGeneres 1/26/58	Johnny Desmond 11/14/21
Hubert DeGivenchy 2/21/27	George Deukmejian 6/6/28
Gloria DeHaven 7/23/25	William Devane 9/5/39
Olivia DeHavilland 7/1/16	Andy Devine 10/7/05
Len Deighton 2/18/29	Danny Devito 11/17/44
Albert Dekker 12/20/05	Dr. William DeVries 12/19/43
W. F. deKlerk 3/18/36	John Dewey 10/20/1859
William Dekooning 4/24/04	Thomas Dewey 3/24/02
Dana Delany 3/13/56	Colleen Dewhurst 6/3/26
Oscar DeLaRenta 7/22/32	Joyce Dewitt 4/23/49
Alicia DeLarrocha 5/23/23	Billy DeWolfe 2/18/07
Dino DeLaurentis 8/8/19	Susan Dey 12/10/52
Gabe Dell 10/7/23	Leonardo de Vinci 4/15/1452
Ron Dellums 11/24/35	Sergei Diaghiler 3/19/1872
Alain Delon 11/8/35	Neil Diamond 1/24/41
Dom Deluise 8/1/33	Princess Diana 7/1/61
Dolores Del Rio 8/3/05	Misha Dichter 9/27/45
William Demarest 2/27/1892	Charles Dickens 2/7/1812
Guy deMaupassant 8/5/1850	Eric Dickerson 9/2/60
Agnes DeMille 9/18/05	Bill Dickey 6/6/07
Cecil B. DeMille 8/12/1881	James Dickey 2/2/23
Jonathan Demme 2/22/44	Angie Dickinson 9/30/31
Philippe DeMontebello 5/16/36	Emily Dickinson 12/10/1830
Rebecca DeMornay 8/29/62	Bo Diddley 12/30/28
Jack Dempsey 6/24/1895	Joan Didion 12/5/35
Jacques Demy 6/5/31	Dan Dierdorf 6/29/49
Catherine Deneuve 10/22/43	Rudoph Diesel 3/18/1858
Robert DeNiro 8/17/43	Marlene Dietrich 12/27/01
Brian Denneny 7/9/40	Howard Dietz 9/8/1896
Patrick Dennis 5/18/21	Joe Diffie 12/28/58

Barry Diller 2/2/42
Phyllis Diller 7/17/17
John Dillinger 6/28/02
Bradford Dillman 4/14/30
Matt Dillon 2/18/64
Dom Dimaggio 2/12/17
Joe Dimaggio 11/25/14
John Dingell 7/8/26
David Dinkins 7/10/27
Christian Dior 1/21/05
Walt Disney 12/5/01
Benjamin Disraeli 12/21/1804
Mike Ditka 10/18/39
Vlade Divac 2/2/68
Richard Dix 7/18/1894
Jeane Dixon 1/5/18
Edward Dmytryk 9/4/08
Mattiwilda Dobbs 7/11/25
Kevin Dobson 3/18/44
Larry Doby 12/13/24
E.L. Doctorow 1/6/31
Christopher Dodd 5/27/44
John Francis Dodge 10/25/1864
Shannen Doherty 4/12/71
Elizabeth Dole 7/20/36
Robert Dole 7/22/23
Chris Doleman 10/16/61
Mickey Dolenz 3/8/45
Dolly Dollar 7/12/62
Pete Domenici 5/7/32
Placido Domingo 1/21/41
Fats Domino 2/26/28
Elinor Donahue 4/19/37
Phil Donahue 12/21/35
Troy Donahue 1/27/37
Sam Donaldson 3/11/34
Robert Donat 3/18/05
Stanley Donen 4/13/24
J.P. Donleavy 4/23/26
Brian Donlevy 2/9/1899
Jeff Donnell 7/10/21
Amanda Donohoe 6/29/62
Donovan 2/10/46
Gen. James Doolittle 12/14/1896

Stephen Dorff 7/29/73
Francoise Dorleac 3/21/42
Diana Dors 10/23/31
Tony Dorsett 4/7/54
Jimmy Dorsey 2/29/04
Lee Dorsey 12/4/26
Tommy Dorsey 11/19/05
Fyodor Dostoevsky 11/11/1821
Abner Doubleday 6/26/1819
Helen-Gahagan Douglas 11/25/00
James "Buster" Douglas 4/7/60
Kirk Douglas............................... 12/9/16
Melvin Douglas 4/5/01
Michael Douglas 9/25/44
Mike Douglas 8/11/25
Paul Douglas 11/4/07
Frederick Douglass 2/7/1817
Brad Dourif 3/18/50
Charles Henry Dow 11/6/1851
Lesley Anne Down 3/17/54
Morton Downey, Jr. 12/9/33
Robert Downey, Jr. 4/4/65
Hugh Downs 2/14/21
Arthur Conan Doyle 5/22/1859
David Doyle 12/1/25
D.J. Dozier 9/21/65
Doug Drabek 7/25/62
Alfred Drake 10/7/14
Tom Drake 8/5/18
Theodore Dreiser 8/27/1871
Marie Dressler 11/9/1869
Elizabeth Drew 11/16/35
Ellen Drew 11/23/15
John Drew 11/13/1853
Clyde Drexler 6/22/62
Richard Dreyfuss 10/29/47
Bobby Driscoll 3/3/36
Capt. William Driver 3/18/1803
Joanne Dru 1/31/23
Peter Drucker 11/9/09
Allen Drury 9/2/18
Don Drysdale 7/23/36
Fred Dryer 7/6/46
Jose Duarte 11/23/26

W.E.B. DuBois 2/23/1868
Jean Dubuffet 7/31/01
Marcel Duchamp 7/28/1887
Eddie Duchin 4/1/09
Peter Duchin 7/28/37
Kevin Duckworth 4/1/64
Frederick Duesenbery 12/6/1876
Howard Duff 11/24/17
Julia Duffy 6/27/51
Patrick Duffy 3/17/49
Val Dufour 2/5/27
Mike Dukakis 11/3/33
Olympia Dukakis 6/20/31
Angier Biddle Duke 11/30/15
Doris Duke 11/22/12
Patty Duke 12/14/46
Vernon Duke 10/10/03
David Dukes 6/6/45
Keir Dullea 5/30/36
Joe Dumars 5/24/63
Daphne DuMaurier 5/13//07
Margaret Dumont 10/20/1889
Faye Dunaway 1/14/41
Paul Laurence Dunbar 6/27/1872
Isadora Duncan 5/27/1878
Sandy Duncan 2/20/46
Irene Dunne 12/20/04
John Gregory Dunne 5/25/32
Mildred Dunnock 1/25/06
Mark Duper 1/25/59
E.I. DuPont 6/24/1771
Marcus Dupree 5/22/64
Roberto Duran 6/16/51
Christopher Durang 1/2/49
Will Durant 11/5/1885
Jimmy Durante 2/10/1893
Deanna Durbin 12/4/21
Charles Durning 2/28/23
Leo Durocher 7/27/06
Friedrich Durrenmatt 1/5/21
Dan Duryea 1/23/07
Nancy Dussault 6/30/36
Charles Dutoit 10/7/36
Robert Duvall 1/5/31

Shelly Duvall 7/7/49
Ann Dvorak 8/2/12
Allan Dwan 4/3/1885
Andrea Dworkin 9/26/46
Pat Dye 11/6/39
Wayne Dyer 5/10/40
Len Dykstra 2/10/63
Bob Dylan 5/24/41
Richard Dysart 3/30/29

E

Sheila E. 12/12/58
Jean Eagels 6/26/1894
Thomas Eagleton 9/4/29
Amelia Earhart 7/24/1898
Steve Earle 1/17/55
Gerald Early 4/12/52
Dale Earnhardt 4/29/40
Wyatt Earp 3/19/1849
Kenny Easley 1/15/59
Jeff East 10/27/57
James O. Eastland 11/28/04
Sheena Easton 4/27/59
Clint Eastwood 5/31/30
Mark Eaton 1/24/57
Abba Eban 2/2/15
Roger Ebert 6/18/42
Buddy Ebsen 4/2/08
Dennis Eckersley 10/3/54
Billy Eckstine 7/8/14
Stefan Edberg 1/19/66
Duane Eddy 4/26/38
Mary Baker Eddy 7/16/1821
Nelson Eddy 6/29/01
Anthony Eden 6/12/1897
Barbara Eden 8/23/34
Thomas Edison 2/11/1847
Dave Edmunds 4/15/44
Prince Edward 3/10/64
Prince Edward 6/23/1894

Blake Edwards 7/26/22
Blue Edwards 10/31/65
Douglas Edwards 7/14/17
Edwin Edwards........................... 8/7/27
James Edwards 11/22/55
Ralph Edwards........................... 6/13/13
Vincent Edwards........................ 7/7/28
Richard Egan 7/29/23
Samantha Eggar 3/5/40
Atom Egoyan............................. 7/19/60
Craig Ehlo 8/11/61
Barbara Ehrenreich 8/26/41
Paul Ehrlich 5/29/32
Lisa Eichhorn 2/4/52
Adolf Eichmann 3/19/06
Alexandre Eiffel 12/15/1832
Jill Eikenberry........................... 2/21/47
Albert Einstein...................... 3/14/1879
Dwight Eisenhower 10/14/1890
John Eisenhower 8/3/22
Mamie Eisenhower 11/14/1896
Sergei Eisenstein 1/23/1898
Michael Eisner 3/7/42
Will Eisner................................... 3/6/17
Stuart Eizenstat 1/15/43
Anita Ekberg............................. 9/29/31
Britt Ekland 10/6/42
Lee Elder 7/14/34
Joycelyn Elders 8/13/33
Florence Eldridge 9/5/01
Sir Edward Elgar 6/2/1857
Larry Elgart............................... 3/20/22
Rosalind Elias 3/13/31
T.S. Eliot 9/26/1888
Queen Elizabeth II 4/21/26
Hector Elizondo 12/22/36
Ellaraino 10/7/38
Henry Ellard 7/21/61
Linda Ellerbee 8/15/44
Duke Ellington 4/29/1899
Cass Elliot.................................. 9/19/43
Bill Elliott 10/8/55
Bob Elliott.................................. 3/26/23
Denholm Elliott 5/31/22

Sam Elliott.................................... 8/9/44
Sean Elliott 2/2/68
William Elliott 6/4/34
Bert Ellis 3/7/64
Perry Ellis 3/3/40
Ralph Waldo Ellison 3/11/14
John Elway 6/28/60
Cary Elwes 10/26/62
Faye Emerson 7/8/17
Ralph Waldo Emerson 5/25/1803
Guillermo Endara 5/12/36
Friedrich Engels 11/28/1820
Alex English............................... 1/5/54
Robert Englund 6/6/49
Brian Eno 5/15/48
John Entwistle 9/10/44
Nora Ephron 5/19/41
Werner Erhard 9/5/35
John Ericson 9/25/26
Erik Erikson 6/15/02
Leif Erikson 10/27/11
John Erman 8/3/35
Sam Ervin 9/27/1896
Julius Erving 2/22/50
Stu Erwin 2/14/02
Christoph Eschenbach.............. 2/20/40
Boomer Esiason 4/17/61
Phil Esposito 2/20/42
Mike Espy 11/3/53
David Essex 7/23/47
Gloria Estefan 9/1/57
Simon Estes 2/2/38
Emilio Estevez 5/12/62
Erik Estrada 3/16/49
Linda Evangelista 5/10/65
Bob Evans 3/30/18
Dale Evans 10/31/12
Dame Edith Evans 2/8/1888
Gene Evans 7/11/22
Janet Evans................................. 8/28/71
Linda Evans 11/18/42
Maurice Evans 6/3/01
Robert Evans............................. 6/29/30
Vince Evans 6/14/55

Rowland Evans, Jr. 4/28/21	Louis Farrakhan 5/11/33
Chad Everett 6/11/37	Charles Farrell 8/9/01
Jim Everett 1/3/63	Eileen Farrell 2/13/20
Don Everly 2/1/37	James T. Farrell 2/27/04
Phil Everly 1/29/39	Mike Farrell 2/6/39
Charles Evers 9/11/22	Sharon Farrell 12/24/49
Medgar Evers 7/2/25	Suzanne Farrell 8/16/45
Chris Evert 12/21/54	Tim Farris 8/16/58
Greg Evigan 10/14/53	Jon Farriss 8/10/62
Celeste Ewell 4/29/19	John Farrow 2/10/06
Tom Ewell 4/29/09	Mia Farrow 2/9/45
Maria Ewing 3/27/50	Brigitte Fassbaender 7/3/39
Patrick Ewing 8/5/62	Howard Fast 11/11/14
	Marshall Faulk 2/26/73
	William Faulkner 9/25/1897

	David Faustin 3/3/74
	Malachi Favors 8/22/37
	Brett Favre 10/10/69
	Farrah Fawcett 2/2/47
Shelley Fabares 1/19/44	Alice Faye 5/5/15
Fabian 2/6/43	Sergei Fedorov 12/13/69
Francoise Fabian 5/10/35	Jules Feiffer 1/26/29
Fabio 3/15/61	Dianne Feinstein 6/22/33
Nanette Fabray 10/27/22	Michael Feinstein 9/7/56
Max Factor III 9/25/45	Buzz Feitshans 1/17/37
John Fahey 2/28/39	Eliot Feld 7/5/42
Douglas Fairbanks 5/23/1883	Fritz Feld 10/15/00
Douglas Fairbanks, Jr 12/9/09	Barbara Feldon 3/12/41
Morgan Fairchild 2/3/50	Tovah Feldshuh 12/27/52
Percy Faith 4/7/08	Martin Feldstein 11/25/39
Marianne Faithfull 12/29/46	Jose Feliciano 9/10/45
Lola Falana 9/11/43	Norman Fell 3/24/25
Nick Faldo 7/18/57	Bob Feller 11/3/18
Peter Falk 9/16/27	Federico Fellini 1/20/20
Oriana Fallaci 6/29/30	Vladimir Feltsman 1/8/52
John Falsey 11/6/51	Freddie Fender 6/4/37
Rev. Jerry Falwell 8/11/33	Edna Ferber 8/15/1887
Ladislas Farago 9/21/06	Francis Ferdinand 12/18/1863
James Farentino 2/24/38	Maynard Ferguson 5/3/28
Donna Fargo 11/10/49	Sarah Ferguson 10/15/59
Dennis Farina 2/29/44	Lawrence Ferlinghetti 3/24/19
Frances Farmer 9/19/13	Enrico Fermi 9/29/01
Richard Farnsworth 9/1/20	Fernandel 5/8/02
Jamie Farr 7/1/34	Geraldine Ferraro 8/26/35

Conchata Ferrell 3/28/43	Gustave Flaubert 12/12/1821
Jose Ferrer 1/8/12	Mick Fleetwood 6/24/47
Mel Ferrer 8/25/17	Richard Fleischer 12/8/16
Lou Ferrigno 11/9/52	Ian Fleming 5/28/08
Bryan Ferry 9/26/45	Joan Fleming 3/27/08
Danny Ferry 10/17/66	Peggy Fleming 7/27/48
Stepin Fetchit 5/30/02	Rhonda Fleming 8/10/23
Arthur Fiedler 12/17/1894	Victor Fleming 2/23/1883
Marshall Field 8/18/1835	Louise Fletcher 7/22/34
Sally Field 11/6/46	Ted Flicker 6/6/30
Cecil Fielder 9/21/63	Curt Flood 1/18/38
Kim Fields 5/12/69	Tom Flores 3/21/37
Totie Fields 5/7/30	Raymond Floyd 9/14/42
W.C. Fields 1/29/1880	Sleepy Floyd 3/6/60
Ralph Fiennes 12/22/62	Errol Flynn 6/20/09
Harvey Fierstein 6/6/54	Larry Flynt 11/1/42
Millard Fillmore 1/7/1800	Nina Foch 4/20/24
Peter Finch 9/28/16	Eugene Fodor (publisher) 10/5/14
Larry Fine 10/5/02	Eugene Fodor 3/5/50
Rollie Finger 8/25/46	Dan Fogelberg 8/13/51
Frank Finlay 8/6/26	Red Foley 6/17/10
Charles Finley 2/22/18	Thomas Foley 3/6/29
Albert Finney 5/9/36	Ken Follett 6/5/49
Harvey Firestone 4/20/1898	Bridget Fonda 1/27/64
Bobby Fischer 3/9/43	Henry Fonda 5/16/05
Dietrich Fischer-Dieskau 5/28/25	Jane Fonda 12/21/37
Larry Fishburne 7/30/61	Peter Fonda 2/23/39
Bobby Fisher 3/9/43	Hiram Fong 10/1/07
Carrie Fisher 10/21/56	Frank Fontaine 4/19/20
Eddie Fisher 8/10/28	Joan Fontaine 10/22/17
Carlton Fisk 12/26/47	Lynn Fontanne 12/6/1887
Emerson Fittipaldi 12/12/46	Margot Fontegn 5/18/19
Barry Fitzgerald 3/10/1888	Wayne Fontes 2/17/39
Ella Fitzgerald 4/25/18	Margot Fonteyn 5/18/19
F. Scott Fitzgerald 9/24/1896	Horton Foote 3/14/16
Geraldine Fitzgerald 11/24/14	Shelby Foote 11/17/16
Cotton Fitzsimmons 10/7/31	Bryan Forber 7/22/26
Marlin Fitzwater 11/24/42	Malcolm S. Forbes 8/19/19
Roberta Flack 2/10/40	Betty Ford 4/8/18
Kirsten Flagstad 7/12/1895	Cris Ford 1/11/49
Father Flanagan 7/13/1886	Edsel Ford 11/6/1893
Fionnula Flanagan 12/10/41	Eileen Otte Ford 3/25/22
Tommy Flanagan 3/16/30	Faith Ford 9/14/64
Susan Flannery 7/31/43	Gerald Ford 7/14/13

Glen Ford	5/1/16
Harrison Ford	7/12/42
Henry Ford	7/30/1863
John Ford	2/1/1895
Paul Ford	11/2/01
"Tennessee" Ernie Ford	2/13/19
Whitey Ford	10/21/28
William Clay Ford	3/14/25
Henry Ford II	9/4/17
George Forman	1/10/49
Milos Forman	2/18/32
E.M. Forster	1/1/1879
Frederick Forsyth	8/25/38
Henderson Forsythe	9/11/17
John Forsythe	1/29/18
Gen. Joe Foss	4/17/15
Bob Fosse	6/23/27
George Foster	12/1/48
Jodie Foster	11/19/62
Phil Foster	3/29/14
Preston Foster	10/24/02
Pete Fountain	7/3/30
Dan Fouts	6/10/51
John Fowles	3/31/26
Edward Fox	4/13/37
Jimmy Fox	10/22/07
Michael J. Fox	6/9/61
Nellie Fox	12/25/27
Robert Foxworth	11/1/41
Redd Foxx	12/9/22
A.J. Foyt	1/16/35
Peter Frampton	4/22/50
Tony Franciosa	10/28/28
Anne Francis	9/16/30
Arlene Francis	10/20/08
Connie Francis	12/12/38
Dick Francis	10/31/20
James Franciscus	1/31/34
Francisco Franco	12/4/1866
Julio Franco	8/23/61
Anne Frank	6/12/29
Barney Frank	3/31/40
Gary Frank	10/9/50
John Frankenheim	2/19/30

Felix Frankfurter	11/15/1882
Aretha Franklin	3/25/42
Benjamin Franklin	1/17/1706
Bonnie Franklin	1/6/44
Mike Frankovich	9/29/10
Mary Frann	2/27/43
Arthur Franz	2/29/20
Dennis Franz	10/28/44
Antonia Fraser	8/27/32
Mike Fratello	2/24/47
Linda Fratianne	8/2/60
William Frawley	2/26/1893
Joe Frazier	1/12/44
Walt Frazier	3/29/45
Stephen Frears	6/20/41
Stan Freberg	8/7/26
World B Free	12/9/53
Arthur Freed	9/9/1894
Bert Freed	11/3/19
James Freed	7/23/30
Mona Freeman	6/9/26
Morgan Freeman	6/1/37
Al Freeman, Jr.	3/21/34
Jim Fregosi	4/4/42
Jeff Freilich	6/29/48
Phyllis Frelich	2/29/44
Marilyn French	11/21/29
Mirella Freni	2/27/35
Anna Freud	12/3/1895
Sigmund Freud	5/5/1856
Matt Frewer	1/4/58
Glenn Frey	11/6/48
Janie Fricke	12/19/47
Betty Friedan	2/4/21
William Friedkin	8/29/39
Mickey Friedman	8/30/44
Milton Friedman	7/31/12
Rudolf Frimi	12/7/1879
Lefty Frizzell	3/31/28
Erich Fromm	3/23/00
David Frost	4/7/39
Robert Frost	3/26/1874
Hayden Fry	2/28/29
Soleil Moon Frye	8/6/76

Travis Fryman 4/25/69
Natalie Fuchs 9/3/52
Carlos Fuentes 11/11/28
Athol Fugard 6/11/32
Alberto Fujimori 7/28/38
William J. Fullbright 4/9/05
Alfred Fuller 1/13/1885
Buckminster Fuller 7/12/1895
Millard Fuller 1/3/35
Samuel Fuller 8/12/12
Annette Funicello 10/22/42
Allen Funt 9/16/14
Richie Furay 5/9/44
Betty Furness 1/3/16
George Furth 12/14/32
Eddy Futch 8/9/11

G

Kenny G. 6/5/56
Martin Gabel 6/19/12
Jean Gabin 5/17/04
Clark Gable 2/1/01
Zsa Zsa Gabor 2/6/19
Eva Gabor. 2/11/25
Peter Gabriel 2/13/50
Roman Gabriel 8/5/40
Nicholas Gage 6/23/39
Dave Gahan 5/9/62
Max Gail 4/5/43
Ernest Gaines 1/15/33
John Kenneth Galbraith 10/15/08
Helen Gallagher 7/19/26
Galileo 2/15/1564
Paul Gallico 7/26/1897
George Gallup 11/18/01
John Galsworth 8/14/1867
James Galway 12/8/39
Rita Gam 4/2/28
Kevin Gamble 11/13/65
Indira Gandhi 11/19/17

Mahatma Gandhi 10/2/1869
Rajiv Gandhi 8/20/44
Joe Garagiola 2/12/26
Greta Garbo 9/18/05
Andy Garcia 4/12/56
Jerry Garcia 8/1/42
Vincent Gardenia 1/7/23
Ava Gardner 12/24/22
Booth Gardner 8/21/36
Erie Stanley Gardner 7/17/1889
Hy Gardner 12/2/04
John Gardner 7/21/33
Allen Garfield 11/22/39
James Garfield 11/19/1831
John Garfield 3/4/13
Art Garfunkel 10/13/42
William Gargan 7/17/05
Judy Garland 6/10/22
Erroll Garner 6/15/21
James Garner 4/7/28
Gale Garnett 7/17/42
Terri Garr 12/11/49
Leif Garrett 11/8/61
Jane Garrison 12/8/51
Sean Garrison 10/19/37
William Lloyd Garrison 12/10/1805
Zina Garrison 11/16/63
Dave Garroway 7/13/13
Greer Garson 9/29/08
Jennie Garth 4/3/72
Marcus Garvey 8/17/1887
Steve Garvey 12/22/48
John Gary 11/29/32
Jose Ortega Gasset 5/9/1883
Vittorio Gassman 9/1/22
Cito Gaston 3/17/44
Larry Gates 9/24/15
Robert Gates 9/25/43
William "Bill" Gates 10/28/55
Larry Gatlin 5/2/49
Paul Gauguin 6/7/1848
Willie Gault 9/5/60
Dick Gautier 10/30/37
John Gavin 4/8/32

Marvin Gaye	4/2/39	Giancarlo Giannini	8/1/42
Crystal Gayle	1/9/51	Andy Gibb	3/5/58
Mitch Gaylord	3/10/61	Barry Gibb	9/1/46
Gloria Gaynor	9/7/48	Maurice Gibb	12/22/49
Janet Gaynor	10/6/06	Robin Gibb	12/22/49
Mitzi Gaynor	9/4/31	Euell Gibbons	9/8/11
Eunice Gayson	3/17/31	Leeza Gibbons	3/26/57
Ben Gazzara	8/28/30	Joe Gibbs	11/25/40
Anthony Geary	5/29/49	Marla Gibbs	6/14/31
Gunther Gebel-Williams	9/12/34	Terri Gibbs	6/15/54
Nicolai Gedda	7/11/25	Khalil Gibran	1/5/1883
Wil Geer	3/9/02	Althea Gibson	8/25/27
David Geffen	2/21/43	Bob Gibson	11/9/35
Lou Gehrig	6/19/03	Charles Gibson	3/9/43
J. Geils	2/20/46	Debbie Gibson	8/31/70
Larry Gelbart	2/25/25	Henry Gibson	9/21/35
Bob Geldof	10/5/51	Hoot Gibson	8/6/1892
Uri Geller	12/20/46	Josh Gibson	12/21/11
Larry Gelman	11/3/30	Kirk Gibson	5/28/57
Jean Genet	12/19/10	Mel Gibson	1/3/56
Leo Genn	8/9/05	Andre Gide	11/22/1869
Bobby Gentry	7/27/44	Sir John Gielgud	4/14/04
Dennis Gentry	2/10/59	Frank Gifford	8/16/30
Teddy Gentry	1/22/52	Kathie Lee Gifford	8/16/53
Boy George	7/14/61	John Gilbert	7/10/1897
Chief Dan George	6/24/1899	Melissa Gilbert	5/8/64
Linda Day George	12/11/46	Sara Gilbert	1/29/75
Phyllis George	6/25/49	Nancy Giles	7/17/60
Susan George	7/26/50	Jack Gilford	7/25/13
Richard Gephart	1/31/41	Brenda Gill	10/4/14
Gil Gerard	1/23/43	Kendall Gill	5/25/68
Richard Gere	8/31/49	Vince Gill	4/12/57
David Gergen	3/9/42	Dizzy Gillespie	10/21/17
George Gershwin	9/26/1898	Anita Gillette	8/16/36
Ira Gershwin	12/6/1896	Mickey Gilley	3/9/36
Vitas Gerulitus	7/26/54	Joe Gilliam	12/29/50
George Gervin	4/27/52	Terry Gilliam	11/22/40
Estelle Getty	7/25/24	Artis Gilmore	8/21/48
Gordon Getty	12/20/33	Virginia Gilmore	7/26/19
J. Paul Getty	12/15/1892	Frank Gilroy	10/13/25
Stan Getz	2/2/27	Peter Gimbel	2/14/28
Alice Ghostley	8/14/26	Hermione Gingold	12/9/1897
Giuseppe Giacomini	9/7/40	Arnold Gingrich	12/5/03
A. Bartlett Giamatti	4/4/38	Newt Gingrich	6/17/43

Allen Ginsberg 6/3/26	Cuba Gooding, Jr. 1/2/68
Ruth Bader Ginsburg 3/15/33	Ace Goodman 1/15/1899
Nikki Giovanni 6/7/43	Benny Goodman 5/30/09
Dorothy Gish 3/11/1898	Ellen Goodman 4/11/41
Lillian Gish 10/14/1896	John Goodman 6/20/52
Robin Givens 11/27/64	Mark Goodson 1/24/15
Jerry Glanville 10/14/41	Charles Goodyear 12/29/1800
Paul Michael Glaser 3/25/42	Evonne Goolagone 7/31/51
Philip Glass 1/31/37	Mikhail Gorbachev 3/2/31
Ron Glass 7/19/45	Raisa Gorbachev 1/5/32
Tom Glavin 5/25/66	Leo Gorcey 6/3/15
Jackie Gleason 2/26/16	David Gordon 7/14/36
John Glenn 7/18/21	Don Gordon 11/13/26
Scott Glenn 1/26/42	Gale Gordon 2/2/06
Sharon Gless 5/31/43	Ruth Gordon 10/30/1896
Crispin Glover 9/20/64	Berry Gordy, Jr. 11/28/29
Danny Glover 7/22/47	Albert Gore 3/31/48
Roger Glover 11/30/45	Lesley Gore 5/2/46
Alma Gluck 5/11/1884	Tipper Gore 8/19/48
George Gobel 5/20/19	Charles Goren 3/4/01
Jean-Luc Godard 12/3/30	Edward Gorey 2/22/25
Paulette Goddard 6/3/11	Maxim Gorky 3/14/1868
Arthur Godfrey 8/31/03	Cliff Gorman 5/31/63
Alexander Godunov 11/28/49	Eydie Gorme 8/16/32
Johann Wolfgang Goethe..... 8/28/1749	Frank Gorshin 4/5/34
Nikolai Gogol 3/31/1809	Marjoe Gortner 1/14/44
Tracey Gold 5/16/69	Freeman Gosden 5/5/1899
Arthur Goldberg 8/8/08	Rich "Goose" Gossage 7/5/51
Leonard Goldberg 1/24/34	Louis Gossett, Jr. 5/27/36
Rube Goldberg 7/4/1883	Brian Gottfried 1/27/52
Whoopi Goldberg 11/13/55	Mike Gottfried 12/17/44
Jeff Goldblum 10/22/52	Chester Gould 11/20/00
William Golding 9/19/11	Elliot Gould 8/29/38
William Goldman 8/12/31	Glenn Gould 9/25/32
Bobby Goldsboro 1/18/41	Harold Gould 12/10/23
Barry Goldwater 1/1/09	Morton Gould 12/10/13
Samuel Goldwyn 8/27/1882	Stephen Jay Gould 9/10/41
Samuel Goldwyn, Jr. 9/7/26	Ray Goulding 3/20/22
Samuel Gompers.................... 1/27/185	Robert Goulet 11/26/33
Pancho Gonzales 5/9/28	Charles Gounod 6/17/1818
Jane Goodall 4/3/34	Curt Gowdy 7/31/19
Wilson Goode 8/19/38	Betty Grable 12/18/16
Dwight Gooden 11/16/64	Mark Grace 6/28/64
Grant Goodeve 7/6/52	Wayne Grady 7/26/57

Steffi Graf	6/14/69
Sue Grafton	4/24/40
Billy Graham	11/7/18
Katharine Graham	6/16/17
Larry Graham	8/14/46
Martha Graham	5/11/1894
Otto Graham	12/6/21
Stedman Graham	3/6/47
Virginia Graham	7/4/12
Gloria Grahame	11/28/25
Fred Grandy	6/29/48
Farley Granger	7/1/25
Red Granger	6/13/03
Stewart Granger	5/6/13
Amy Grant	11/25/60
Cary Grant	1/18/04
Gary Grant	4/21/65
Harvey Grant	7/4/65
Horace Grant	7/4/65
Hugh Grant	9/9/60
Kathryn Grant	11/25/33
Lee Grant	10/31/30
Ulysses S. Grant	4/27/1822
Gunter Grass	10/16/27
Samuel L. Gravely, Jr.	6/4/22
Earl Graves	1/9/35
Peter Graves	3/18/26
Barry Gray	7/2/16
Erin Gray	1/7/52
Linda Gray	9/12/41
Kathryn Grayson	2/9/23
William Gray III	8/20/40
Rocky Graziano	6/7/22
Buddy Greco	8/14/26
Jose Greco	12/23/18
Juliette Greco	2/7/27
Andrew Greeley	2/5/28
A.C. Green	10/4/63
Adolph Green	12/2/15
Bob Green	3/10/47
Brian Austin Green	7/15/73
Dallas Green	8/4/34
Dennis Green	2/17/49
Graham Green	10/2/04

Hubert Green	12/28/46
"Mean" Joe Green	9/24/46
Rev. Al Green	4/13/46
Rickey Green	8/18/54
Hank Greenberg	1/1/11
Lorne Greene	2/12/15
Shecky Greene	4/8/26
Jeff Greenfield	6/10/43
Alan Greenspan	3/6/26
Sydney Greenstreet	12/27/1879
L.C. Greenwood	2/2/49
Lee Greenwood	10/27/42
Germaine Greer	1/29/39
Jane Greer	9/9/24
Michael Greer	9/19/17
Forrest Gregg	10/18/33
Dick Gregory	10/12/32
James Gregory	12/23/11
Wayne Gretzky	1/26/61
Joel Grey	4/11/32
Zane Grey	1/31/1875
David Alan Grier	6/30/56
Johnny Grier	4/16/47
Pamela Grier	5/26/49
Roosevelt Grier	7/14/32
Bob Griese	2/3/45
Ken Griffey, Jr.	11/21/69
Ken Griffey, Sr.	4/10/50
Archie Griffin	8/24/54
John Howard Griffin	6/16/20
Merv Griffin	7/6/25
Andy Griffith	6/1/26
Corinne Griffith	11/24/1896
D.W. Griffith	1/22/1875
Melanie Griffith	8/9/57
Florence Griffith-Joyner	12/21/59
Tammy Grimes	1/30/36
Juan Gris	3/13/1887
John Grisham	2/8/55
Marquis Grissom	4/17/67
Virgil Grissom	4/3/26
George Grizzard	4/1/28
Charles Grodin	4/21/35
Matt Groening	2/15/54

Steve Grogan 7/24/53
Mary Gross 3/25/53
Michael Gross 6/21/47
George Grosz 7/26/1895
Harry Guardino 12/23/25
Aldo Gucci 5/26/09
Bob Guccione 12/17/30
Heinz Guderian 6/17/1888
Pedro Guerrero 6/29/56
Christopher Guest 2/5/48
Ron Guidry 8/28/50
Robert Guillaume 11/30/37
Ozzie Guillen 1/20/64
Sir Alec Guiness 4/2/14
Cathy Guisewite 9/5/50
Bryant Gumbel 9/29/48
Greg Gumbel 5/3/46
Moses Gunn 10/2/29
Hal Gurnee 1/25/35
A.R. Gurney, Jr. 11/1/30
Arlo Guthrie 7/10/47
Janet Guthrie............................... 3/7/38
Tyrone Guthrie 7/2/00
Woody Guthrie 7/14/12
Steve Guttenberg 8/24/58
Jasmin Guy 3/10/64
Tony Gwynn.............................. 5/9/60
Fred Gwynne 7/10/26

H

Luke Haas 4/16/76
Shelley Hack 7/6/49
Buddy Hackett 8/31/24
Joan Hackett 3/1/42
Gene Hackman.......................... 1/30/31
Sammy Hagar.......................... 10/13/49
Jean Hagen 8/3/23
Uta Hagen 6/12/19
Merle Haggard 4/6/37
Dan Haggarty 11/19/41

Marvin Hagler........................... 5/23/54
Larry Hagman 9/21/31
Charles Haid 6/2/43
Alexander Haig 12/2/24
Arthur Hailey 5/5/20
Corey Haim 12/23/71
George Halas 2/2/1895
David Halberstam 4/10/34
H.R. Haldeman 10/27/26
Alan Hale 2/10/1892
Barbara Hale 4/18/22
Alex Haley 8/11/21
Arthur Haley 4/5/20
Bill Haley................................... 7/6/25
Charles Haley 1/6/64
Jack Haley 8/10/00
Anthony Michael Hall.............. 4/14/68
Arsenio Hall............................. 2/12/56
Daryl Hall 10/11/48
Deidre Hall 10/31/49
Gus Hall 10/8/10
Janice Hall 9/28/53
Jerry Hall 7/2/56
Jon Hall 2/23/13
Joyce Clyde Hall 8/29/1891
Juanita Hall 11/6/01
Monty Hall 8/25/23
Tom T. Hall 5/25/36
Edmund Halley 11/8/1656
Philippe Halsman 5/2/06
Halston 4/23/32
Veronica Hamel 11/20/45
Dorothy Hamill 7/26/56
Mark Hamill 9/25/51
Alexander Hamilton............. 1/11/1757
Carrie Hamilton 12/5/63
Donald Hamilton 3/24/16
George Hamilton 8/12/39
Linda Hamilton 9/26/57
Margaret Hamilton 12/9/02
Scott Hamilton 8/28/58
Harry Hamlin 10/30/51
Marvin Hamlisch 6/2/44
Dag Hammarskjold 7/29/05

Hammer 3/30/63	George Harrison 2/25/43
Armand Hammer 5/21/1898	Gregory Harrison 5/31/50
Jan Hammer 4/17/48	Rex Harrison 3/5/08
Oscar Hammerstein 7/12/1895	Deborah Harry 7/1/45
Dashiell Hammett 5/27/1894	Doris Hart 6/20/25
Susan Hampshire 5/12/42	Gary Hart 11/28/36
Dan Hampton 9/19/57	Johnny Hart 2/18/31
Lionel Hampton 4/12/13	Lorenz Hart 5/2/1895
Herbie Hancock 4/12/40	Mary Hart 11/8/51
John Hancock 1/12/1736	Melissa Joan Hart 4/28/76
George Fredrick Handel 2/23/1685	Mickey Hart 9/11/43
W.C. Handy 11/16/1873	Moss Hart 10/24/04
Tom Hanks 7/9/56	William S. Hart 12/6/1872
Bill Hanna 7/14/10	Bill Hartack 12/9/32
Daryl Hannah 12/3/61	Huntington Hartford 4/18/11
Tim Haraway 9/12/66	Mariette Hartley 6/21/40
Ann Harding 8/17/04	David Hartman 5/19/35
Warren Harding 11/2/1865	Elizabeth Hartman 12/23/41
Anfernee Hardaway 7/18/72	Lisa Hartman 6/1/56
Cedric Hardwicke 2/19/1893	John Harvard 11/26/1607
Oliver Hardy 1/18/1892	Laurence Harvey 10/1/28
Thomas Hardy 6/2/1840	Paul Harvey 9/4/18
Billy James Hargis 8/3/25	Ernie Harwell 1/25/18
Mata Hari 8/7/1876	Peter Haskell 10/15/34
Keith Haring 5/4/58	Clem Haskins 8/11/44
Thomas Harkin 11/19/39	David Hasselhoff 7/17/52
Jean Harlow 3/3/11	Signe Hasso 8/15/15
Mark Harmon 9/2/51	Alcee Hastings 9/5/36
Ronnie Harmon 5/7/64	Orrin Hatch 3/22/34
Sheldon Harnick 4/30/24	Richard Hatch 5/21/46
Derek Harper 10/13/61	Charles Hatcher 7/1/39
Ron Harper 1/20/64	Richard Hatcher 7/10/33
Valerie Harper 8/22/40	Mark Hatfield 7/12/22
Woody Harrelson 7/23/61	Rutger Hauer 1/23/44
Pat Harrington 8/13/29	Vaclav Havel 10/5/36
Ed Harris 11/28/50	Richie Havens 1/21/41
Emmylou Harris 4/2/48	June Haver 6/10/26
Franco Harris 3/7/50	John Havlicek 4/8/40
Frank Harris 2/14/1856	June Havoc 11/8/16
Julie Harris 12/2/25	Augustus Hawkins 8/31/07
Lou Harris 1/6/21	Connie Hawkins 7/17/42
Phil Harris 6/24/06	Hersey Hawkins 9/29/65
Richard Harris 10/1/33	Jack Hawkins 9/14/10
Rosemary Harris 9/19/30	Howard Hawks 5/30/1898

Goldie Hawn 11/21/45
Nathaniel Hawthorne 7/4/1804
S.I. Hayakawa 7/18/06
Sessue Hayakawa 6/10/1889
Joseph Hayden 3/31/1732
Melissa Hayden 4/25/28
Russell Hayden 6/12/12
Sterling Hayden 3/26/16
Tom Hayden 12/11/40
Arthur Garfield Hayes 12/12/1881
Elvin Hayes 11/17/53
Gabby Hayes 5/7/1855
Helen Hayes 10/10/00
Isaac Hayes 8/20/42
Lester Hayes 1/22/55
Peter Lind Hayes 6/25/15
Rutherford B. Hayes 10/4/1822
Woody Hayes 2/14/13
Dick Haymes 9/13/17
Robert Hays 7/24/47
Will Hays 11/4/1885
Leland Hayward 9/13/02
Louis Hayward 3/19/09
Susan Hayward 6/30/19
Spencer Haywood 4/22/49
Rita Hayworth 10/17/18
Edith Head 10/28/07
Glenne Aimee Headly 3/31/58
John Heard 3/7/45
Tommy Hearns 10/18/58
Patty Hearst 2/20/54
William Randolph Hearst 4/29/1863
William Randolph Hearst, Jr. ... 1/27/08
Joey Heatherton 9/14/44
Eileen Heckart 3/29/19
Tippi Hedren 1/19/35
Howard Heflin 6/19/21
Van Heflin 12/13/10
Christie Hefner 11/8/52
Hugh Hefner 4/9/26
Georg Friedrich Hegel 8/27/1770
Eric Heiden 6/14/58
Horace Heidt 5/21/01
Jascha Heifetz 2/2/01

Tom Heinsohohn 8/26/34
Henry J. Heinz 10/11/1844
H.J. Heinz III 7/10/08
John W. Heisman 10/23/1869
Joseph Heller 5/1/23
Lillian Hellman 6/20/05
Katherine Helmond 7/5/34
Jesse Helms 10/18/21
Heloise 4/15/51
Ernest Hemingway 7/21/1899
Mariel Hemingway 11/22/61
David Hemmings 11/21/41
Sherman Hemsley 2/1/38
Fletch Henderson 12/18/1897
Florence Henderson 2/14/34
Jimmy Henderson 5/20/54
Rickey Henderson 12/25/58
Skitch Henderson 1/27/18
Barbara Hendricks 11/20/48
Jimi Hendrix 11/27/42
Sonja Henie 4/8/12
Beth Henley 5/8/52
Don Henley 7/22/47
Mike Henneman 12/11/61
Marilu Henner 4/6/53
Doug Henning 5/3/47
Paul Henreid 1/10/08
Henry VIII 6/28/1491
Buck Henry 12/9/30
O. Henry 9/11/1862
Patrick Henry 5/29/1736
Jim Henson 9/24/36
Matthew Henson 8/8/1866
Audrey Hepburn 5/4/29
Katharine Hepburn 11/8/07
Herblock 10/13/09
Jerry Herman 7/10/33
Pee Wee Herman 8/27/52
Woody Herman 5/16/13
Keith Hernandez 10/10/53
Mark Herndon 5/11/55
Carolina Herrera 1/8/39
James Herriot 10/3/16
Edward Herrmann 7/21/43

John Hersey	6/17/14
Barbara Hershey	2/5/48
Milton Hershey	9/13/1857
Orel Hershiser	9/16/58
Jean Hersholt	7/12/1886
John Daniel Hertz	4/10/1879
Werner Herzog	9/6/42
Whitey Herzog	2/26/31
Rudolf Hess	4/26/1894
Hermann Hesse	7/2/1877
Howard Hesseman	2/27/40
Charlton Heston	10/4/24
Don Hewitt	12/14/22
Thor Heyerdahl	10/6/14
Darryl Hickman	7/28/31
Dwayne Hickman	5/18/34
Wild Bill Hickok	5/27/1837
Hilly Hicks	5/4/50
George V. Higgins	11/13/39
Hildegrade	2/1/06
Anita Hill	7/30/56
Arthur Hill	8/1/22
Benny Hill	1/21/25
Calvin Hill	1/2/47
Grant Hill	10/5/72
George Roy Hill	12/20/22
Lenora Mae Hill	6/2/37
Patty Smith Hill	3/27/1868
Arthur Hiller	11/22/23
Wendy Hiller	8/15/12
John Hillerman	12/20/32
Tony Hillerman	5/27/25
Daniel W. Hillis	9/25/56
Carla Hills	1/3/34
Conrad Hilton	12/25/1887
Heinrich Himmler	10/7/00
John Hinckley, Jr.	5/29/55
Paul Hindemith	11/16/1895
Duncan Hines	3/26/1880
Earl Fatha Hines	12/28/05
Gregory Hines	2/14/46
Jerome Hines	11/9/21
Pat Hingle	7/19/24
Emperor Hirohito	4/29/01
Judd Hirsch	3/15/35
Al Hirschfeld	6/21/03
Al Hirt	11/7/22
Alger Hiss	11/11/04
Alfred Hitchcock	8/13/1899
Shere Hite	11/2/42
Adolf Hitler	4/20/1889
Don Ho	8/13/30
Thomas Hobbes	4/5/1588
Oveta Culp Hobby	1/19/05
Laura Z. Hobson	6/19/00
David Hockney	7/9/37
Craig Hodges	6/27/60
Gil Hodges	4/4/24
John Hodiak	4/16/14
Jimmy Hoffa	2/14/13
Eric Hoffer	7/25/02
Abbie Hoffman	11/30/36
Alice Hoffman	3/16/52
Dustin Hoffman	8/8/37
Ben Hogan	8/13/12
Hulk Hogan	8/11/53
Hal Holbrook	2/17/25
William Holden	4/17/18
Geoffrey Holder	8/1/30
Billie Holiday	4/7/15
Brian Holland	2/15/41
Jennifer Holliday	10/19/60
Judy Holliday	6/21/22
Polly Holliday	7/2/37
Earl Holliman	9/11/28
Ernest Hollings	1/1/22
Stanley Holloway	10/1/1890
Buddy Holly	9/7/36
Celeste Holm	4/29/19
Ian Holm	9/12/31
Larry Holmes	11/3/49
Oliver Wendell Holmes	8/29/1809
Rupert Holmes	2/24/47
Tim Holt	2/5/18
Lou Holtz	1/6/37
Evander Holyfield	10/19/62
Red Holzman	8/10/20
Skip Homeier	10/5/30

Winslow Homer 2/24/1836	Frank Howard 8/8/36
John B. Hood 6/1/1831	Juwan Howard 2/7/73
Sidney Hook 12/20/02	Ken Howard 3/28/44
John Lee Hooker 8/22/17	Leslie Howard 4/24/1893
Joseph Hooker 11/13/1814	Moe Howard 6/19/1897
Bell Hooks 9/25/52	Ron Howard 3/1/54
Benjamin Hooks 1/31/25	Shemp Howard 3/17/00
Jan Hooks 4/23/57	Susan Howard 1/28/43
Burt Hooton 2/7/50	Trevor Howard 9/29/16
Herbert Hoover 8/10/1874	Gordon Howe 3/31/28
J. Edgar Hoover 1/1/1895	James Wong Howe 8/28/1899
Bob Hope 5/29/03	Steve Howe 4/8/47
Anthony Hopkins 12/31/37	C. Thomas Howell 12/9/66
Bo Hopkins 2/2/42	Sally Ann Howes 7/20/30
John Hopkins 5/19/1795	Beth Howland 5/28/47
Lightnin Hopkins 3/15/07	Lamarr Hoyt 1/1/55
Miriam Hopkins 10/18/02	Freddie Hubbard 4/7/38
Telma Hopkins 10/28/48	L. Ron Hubbard 3/13/11
Dennis Hopper 5/17/36	David Huddleston 9/17/30
Edward Hopper 7/22/1882	Rock Hudson 11/17/25
Hedda Hopper 6/2/1890	Leon Huff 4/8/42
Paul Horn 3/17/30	Sam Huff 10/4/34
Jeff Hornacek 5/3/63	Barnard Hughes 7/16/15
Lena Horne 6/30/17	Charles Evans Hughes 4/11/1862
Marilyn Horne 1/16/34	Howard Hughes 12/24/05
Bruce Hornsby 11/23/54	Langston Hughes 2/1/02
Paul Hornung 12/23/35	Victor Hugo 2/25/1802
Vladimir Horowitz 10/1/04	Wayne H. Huizenga 12/29/39
Edward Everett Horton 3/18/1886	Tom Hulce 12/6/53
Johnny Horton 4/30/27	Bobby Hull 1/3/39
Robert Horton 7/29/24	Burt Hull 8/9/64
Willie Horton (Baseball) 10/18/42	Rex Humbard 8/13/19
Bob Hoskins 10/26/42	Engelbert Humperdinck 5/3/36
Morihiro Hosokawa 1/14/38	Derek Humphrey 3/29/30
A.E. Hotchner 6/28/20	Hubert Humphrey 5/27/11
Harry Houdini 3/24/1887	Gayle Hunnicutt 2/6/43
Charlie Hough 1/4/48	Bunker Hunt 2/22/26
Katharine Houghton 3/10/45	E. Howard Hunt 10/9/18
Ralph Houk 8/9/19	H.L. Hunt 2/17/1889
John Houseman 9/22/02	Helen Hunt 6/15/63
Sam Houston 3/2/1793	Lamar Hunt 8/2/32
Whitney Houston 8/9/63	Linda Hunt 4/2/45
Betty Howar 9/27/34	Marsha Hunt 10/17/17
Curly Howard 10/22/03	Alberta Hunter 4/1/1897

Dale Hunter 7/31/60
Evan Hunter 10/15/26
Holly Hunter 3/20/58
Jeffery Hunter 11/25/27
Jim "Catfish" Hunter 4/18/46
Kim Hunter 11/12/22
Ross Hunter 5/6/24
Tab Hunter 7/11/31
Chet Huntley 12/10/11
James Hurd 8/2/45
Bobby Hurley 6/28/71
John Hurt 1/22/40
Mary Beth Hurt 9/26/48
William Hurt 3/20/50
Saddam Hussein 4/28/37
King Hussein of Jordan 11/14/35
Olivia Hussey 4/17/51
Ruth Hussey 10/30/14
Anjelica Huston 7/8/51
John Huston 8/5/06
Walter Huston 4/5/1884
Barbara Hutton 11/14/12
Betty Hutton 2/26/21
Jim Hutton 5/31/38
Lauren Hutton 11/17/44
Robert Hutton 6/11/20
Timothy Hutton 8/16/50
Wilfred Hyde-White 5/12/03
Martha Hyer 8/10/24
Earle Hyman 10/11/26
Chrissie Hynde 9/7/57

Lee Iacocca 10/15/24
Janis Ian 5/7/50
Henrik Ibsen 3/20/1828
Eric Idle 3/29/43
Billy Idol 11/30/55
Ramez Idriss 9/11/11
Julio Iglesias 9/23/43

Reverend Ike 6/1/35
Iman 7/25/55
Lindy Infante 5/27/40
William Inge 5/3/13
Marty Ingels 3/9/36
James Ingram 2/16/56
Roy Innis 6/6/34
Daniel Inouye 9/7/24
Eugene Ionesco 11/26/12
Jill Ireland 4/24/36
John Ireland 1/30/15
Jeremy Irons 9/19/48
John Irvin 3/2/42
Amy Irving 9/10/53
Michael Irving 3/5/66
Bill Irwin 4/11/50
Hale Irwin 6/3/45
Christopher Isherwood 8/26/04
Kelly Isley 12/25/37
Robert Isley 4/1/39
Ronald Isley 5/21/41
Raghib Ismail 11/18/69
Dan Issel 10/25/48
Eugene Istomin 11/26/25
Lance Ito 8/2/50
Jose Iturbi 11/28/1895
Burl Ives 6/14/09
Charles Ives 10/20/1874
Judith Ivey 9/4/51

L.L. Cool J. 1/14/68
Wolfman Jack 1/21/38
Jackee 8/14/56
Alan Jackson 10/17/58
Andrew Jackson 3/15/1767
Anne Jackson 9/3/26
Bo Jackson 11/30/62
Glenda Jackson 5/9/37
Gordon Jackson 12/19/23

Hurricane Jackson	8/9/31
Jackie Jackson	5/4/51
Janet Jackson	5/16/66
Jermaine Jackson	12/11/54
Jesse Jackson	10/8/41
Joe Jackson	8/11/55
Kate Jackson	10/29/49
Keith Jackson	10/18/28
Keith Jackson (football)	4/19/65
LaToya Jackson	5/29/56
Mahalia Jackson	10/26/11
Mark Jackson	4/1/65
Marlon Jackson	3/12/57
Mary Jackson	11/22/10
Maynard Jackson	3/23/38
Michael Jackson	8/29/58
Phil Jackson	9/17/45
Randy Jackson	10/31/61
Reggie Jackson	5/18/46
Shoeless Joe Jackson	7/16/1887
Stonewall Jackson	1/21/1824
Stu Jackson	12/11/55
Tito Jackson	10/15/53
Victoria Jackson	8/2/59
Helen Hull Jacob	8/6/08
John Jacob	12/16/34
Derek Jacobi	10/22/38
Lou Jacobi	12/28/13
Oswald Jacoby	12/8/02
Richard Jaeckel	10/10/30
Andrea Jaeger	6/4/65
Rona Jaffe	6/12/32
Sam Jaffe	3/8/1893
Stanley Jaffe	7/31/40
Bianca Jagger	5/2/45
Dean Jagger	11/7/03
Mick Jagger	7/26/43
Jaromir Jagr	2/15/72
John Jakes	3/31/32
Ahmad Jamal	7/2/30
Malcolm Jamal-Warner	8/18/70
Harry James	3/15/16
Henry James	4/15/1843
Jesse James	9/5/1847
Rick James	2/1/48
Judith Jamison	5/10/34
Elizabeth Janeway	10/7/13
Byron Janis	3/24/28
Joan Janis	11/16/26
Emil Jannings	7/23/1884
David Jannsen	3/27/31
Dan Jansen	6/17/65
Don January	11/20/29
Al Jardine	9/3/42
Claude Jarman, Jr.	9/27/34
Maurice Jarre	9/13/24
Al Jarreau	3/12/40
Keith Jarrett	3/8/45
Vernon Jarrett	6/19/21
Tom Jarriel	12/29/44
Robert Jarvik	5/11/46
Jacob Javits	5/18/04
Thomas Jefferson	4/13/1743
Anne Jeffreys	1/26/23
Mae Jemison	10/17/56
Ferguson Jenkins	12/13/43
Bruce Jenner	10/28/49
Peter Jennings	7/29/38
Waylon Jennings	6/15/37
George Jessel	4/3/1898
Joan Jett	9/22/59
Norman Jewison	7/21/26
Ann Jillian	1/29/51
Billy Joel	5/9/49
Charles Joffe	7/16/29
Robert Joffrey	12/24/30
Ingemar Johansson	9/22/32
Dr. John	11/21/40
Elton John	3/25/47
Tommy John	5/22/43
Gordon Johncock	8/5/36
Glynis Johns	10/5/23
Jasper Johns	5/15/30
Andrew Johnson	12/29/1808
Ben Johnson	6/13/18
Betsey Johnson	8/10/42
Beverly Johnson	10/13/52
Bruce Johnson	6/27/44

Dennis Johnson 9/18/54
Don Johnson 12/15/49
Ervin "Magic" Johnson 8/14/59
George Johnson 5/17/53
Jack Johnson 3/31/1878
Jimmy Johnson 7/16/43
John H. Johnson 1/19/18
Kevin Johnson 3/4/66
Lady Bird Johnson 12/22/12
Larry Johnson 3/14/69
Luci Baines Johnson 7/2/47
Lynda Bird Johnson 3/19/44
Lyndon Baines Johnson 8/27/08
Nunnally Johnson 12/5/1897
Rafer Johnson 8/18/35
Reginald Vel Johnson 8/16/52
Robert L. Johnson 4/8/46
Samuel Johnson 9/18/1709
Van Johnson 8/25/16
Vinnie Johnson 9/1/56
Walter Johnson 11/6/1887
Ben Johnson (Athlete) 12/30/61
Al Jolson 5/26/1886
Allan Jones 10/14/07
Bobby Jones 3/17/02
Brian Jones 2/26/43
Buck Jones 12/4/1889
Carolyn Jones 4/28/33
Casey Jones 3/14/1864
Christopher Jones 8/18/41
Davey Jones 12/30/46
Deacon Jones 4/18/34
Dean Jones 1/25/36
Ed "Too Tall" Jones 2/23/51
George Jones 9/12/31
Grace Jones 5/19/52
Henry Jones 9/1/12
Howard Jones 2/23/55
Jack Jones 11/11/38
James Jones 11/6/21
James Earl Jones 1/17/31
Jennifer Jones 3/2/19
John Paul Jones............................ 1/3/46
K.C. Jones 5/25/32

L.Q. Jones 8/19/27
Leroi Jones 10/7/34
Parnelli Jones 8/12/33
Preston Jones 4/7/36
Quincy Jones............................ 3/14/33
Rickie Lee Jones........................ 11/8/54
Sam Jones 6/24/33
Shirley Jones 3/31/34
Spike Jones 12/14/11
Terry Jones 2/1/42
Tom Jones.................................... 2/17/28
Tom Jones (Singer)..................... 6/7/40
Tommy Lee Jones...................... 9/15/46
Erica Jong 3/26/42
Janis Joplin 1/19/43
Scott Joplin 11/24/1868
Barbara Jordan 2/21/36
Hamilton Jordan 9/21/44
Louis Jordan 7/8/08
Michael Jordan 2/17/63
Vernon Jordan 8/15/35
Christine Jorgensen 5/30/26
Victor Jory 11/23/03
Josephine (Bonaparte) 6/24/1763
Allyn Joslyn 7/21/01
Louis Jourdan 6/19/20
James Joyce 2/2/1882
Wally Joyner 6/16/62
Jackie Joyner-Kersee 3/3/62
Benito Juarez........................... 3/21/1806
Naomi Judd 1/11/46
Wynonna Judd 5/30/64
Raul Julia 3/9/40
Carl Jung 7/26/1875
Curt Jurgens.............................. 12/12/15
Sonny Jurgensen 8/23/34
David Justice............................. 4/14/66

Dmitri Kabalevsky 12/30/04

Pauline Kael	6/19/19
Franz Kafka	7/2/1883
Meir Kahane	8/1/32
Madeline Kahn	9/29/42
Chiang Kai-Shek	10/31/1886
Madam Chiang Kai-Shek	6/5/1857
Toshiki Kaifu	1/2/31
Karen Kain	3/29/51
Henry J. Kaiser	5/9/1882
Marvin Kalb	6/9/30
Al Kaline	12/19/34
Norma Kamali	6/27/45
Ida Kaminska	9/4/1899
Steven Kanaly	3/14/46
Kiri Te Kanawa	3/6/47
Wassily Kandinsky	12/4/1866
Bob Kane	10/24/16
Carol Kane	6/18/52
Garson Kanin	11/24/12
Hal Kanter	12/18/18
Paul Kantner	3/12/42
Mickey Kantor	8/7/39
Gabe Kaplan	3/31/45
Donna Karan	10/2/48
John Karlen	5/28/33
Boris Karloff	11/23/1887
Anatoly Karpov	5/23/51
Alex Karras	7/15/35
Yousef Karsh	12/23/08
Lawrence Kasdan	1/14/49
Gary Kasparov	4/13/63
Nancy Kassebaum	6/29/32
William Katt	2/16/51
Stanley Kauffman	4/24/16
Andy Kaufman	1/17/49
George S. Kaufman	11/16/1889
Phil Kaufman	10/23/36
Julie Kavner	9/7/51
Danny Kaye	1/18/13
Sammy Kaye	3/13/13
Elia Kazan	9/7/09
Lainie Kazan	5/16/42
Stacy Keach	6/2/41
Buster Keaton	10/4/1896

Diane Keaton	1/5/46
Michael Keaton	9/9/51
John Keats	10/31/1795
Howard Keel	4/13/19
Ruby Keeler	8/25/09
Sam Keen	11/23/31
Mike Keenan	10/21/49
Bob Keeshan	6/27/27
Garrison Keillor	8/7/42
Harvey Keitel	5/13/39
Brian Keith	11/14/21
David Keith	8/8/54
George Kell	8/23/22
Helen Keller	6/27/1880
Martha Keller	1/28/44
Sally Kellerman	6/2/37
DeForest Kelley	1/20/20
Kitty Kelley	4/4/42
W.K. Kellogg	4/7/1860
Chris Kelly	5/1/78
Emmett Kelly	12/9/1898
Gene Kelly	8/23/12
Jim Kelly	2/14/60
Patrick Kelly	9/24/54
Patsy Kelly	1/12/10
Petra Kelly	11/29/47
Princess Grace Kelly	11/12/29
Sharon Pratt Kelly	1/30/44
Walt Kelly	8/25/13
Jack Kemp	7/13/35
Shawn Kemp	11/26/69
Anthony Kennedy	7/23/36
Arthur Kennedy	2/17/14
Burt Kennedy	9/3/22
Caroline Kennedy	11/27/57
Edward Kennedy	2/22/32
Ethel Kennedy	4/11/28
George Kennedy	2/18/25
John F. Kennedy	5/29/17
Joseph Kennedy	9/6/1888
Joseph P. Kennedy	9/24/52
Nigel Kennedy	12/28/56
Robert F. Kennedy	11/20/25
Rose Kennedy	6/22/1890

John Kennedy, Jr. 11/25/60	Jean-Claude Killey 8/30/43
Jayne Kennedy-Overton 10/27/51	Billy Kilmer 9/5/39
Patsy Kensit 3/4/68	Val Kilmer 12/31/59
Rockwell Kent 6/21/1882	James J. Kilpatrick 11/1/20
Stan Kenton 2/19/12	Bobby Kimbal 3/29/47
Ken Kercheval 7/15/35	Bo Kimble 4/9/66
Kirk Kerkorian 6/6/17	Jamaica Kincaid 5/25/49
Jerome Kern 1/17/1885	Alan King 12/26/27
Joanna Kerns 2/12/53	Albert King 4/25/23
Jack Kerouac 3/12/22	B.B. King 9/16/25
Deborah Kerr 9/30/21	Ben E. King 9/28/38
Jean Kerr 7/10/23	Bernard King 12/4/56
John Kerr 11/15/31	Billy Jean King 11/22/43
Red Kerr 8/17/32	Carole King 2/9/41
Steve Kerr 9/27/65	Don King 12/6/32
Nancy Kerrigan 10/13/69	Frank King 6/11/1883
Bob Kerry 8/27/43	Larry King 11/19/33
John Kerry 12/11/43	Perry King 4/30/48
Jerome Kersey 6/26/62	Stacey King 1/29/67
Nik Kershaw 3/1/58	Stephen King 9/21/47
Larry Kert 12/5/30	Martin Luther King, Jr 1/15/29
Lance Kerwin 11/6/60	Ben Kingsley 12/31/43
Kent Kesey 9/17/35	Michael Kinsley 3/9/51
Hal Ketchum 4/9/53	Sidney Kingsley 10/18/06
Hank Ketcham 3/14/20	Barbara Kingsolver 4/8/55
Dr. Jack Kevorkian 5/26/28	Kathleen Kinmont 2/3/67
Ted Key 8/25/12	Alfred Kinsey 6/23/1894
Frances Keyes 7/21/1885	Nastassia Kinski 1/24/60
John Maynard Keynes 6/5/1883	Rudyard Kipling 12/30/1865
Evelyn Keys 11/20/19	Bruno Kirby 4/28/48
Persis Khambata 10/2/50	Durward Kirby 8/24/12
Chaka Khan 3/23/53	George Kirby 6/8/23
Adnan Khashoggi 7/25/35	Lisa Kirk 2/25/25
Ayatollah Khomeini 5/17/00	Phyllis Kirk 9/18/29
Nikita Khrushchev 4/17/1894	Gelsey Kirkland 12/29/52
Jason Kidd 3/23/73	Lane Kirkland 3/12/22
Michael Kidd 8/12/19	Jeanne Kirkpatrick 12/19/26
Margot Kidder 10/17/48	James Kirkwood 8/22/30
Nicole Kidman 6/21/67	Don Kirshner 4/17/34
Soren Kierkegaard 5/5/1813	Henry Kissinger 5/27/23
Krzysztof Kieslowski 6/27/41	Tom Kite 12/9/49
Richard Kiley 3/31/22	Eartha Kitt 1/26/28
Dorothy Kilgallen 7/3/13	Paul Klee 12/18/1879
Hermon Killebrow 6/29/36	Calvin Klein 11/19/42

Robert Klein 2/8/42
Joe Kleine 1/4/62
John Kleiser 7/20/46
Otto Klemperer 5/14/1885
Werner Klemperer 3/22/20
Kevin Kline 10/24/47
John Kluge 9/21/14
Jack Klugman 4/27/22
Fletcher Knebel 10/1/11
Evel Knievel 10/17/39
Bobby Knight 10/25/40
Gladys Knight 5/28/44
John Knight 10/26/1894
Ray Knight 12/28/52
Shirley Knight 7/5/36
Ted Knight 12/7/23
Chuck Knoll 1/5/32
Alfred A. Knopf 9/12/1892
Mark Knopfler 8/12/49
Don Knotts 7/21/24
Alexander Knox 1/16/07
Chuck Knox 4/27/32
Oliver Knussen 6/12/52
Ed Koch 12/12/24
Howard Koch 4/11/16
Teddy Kolleck 5/27/11
Jon Koncak 5/17/63
C. Everett Koop 10/16/16
Mary Jo Kopechne 7/26/40
Bernard Kopell 6/21/33
Arthur L. Kopit 5/10/37
Ted Koppel 2/8/40
Olga Korbut 5/16/55
Alexander Korda 9/15/1893
Harvey Korman 2/15/27
Bernie Kosar 11/25/63
Jerzy Kosinski 6/14/33
Andre Kostelanetz 12/22/01
Rich Kottite 10/13/42
Yaphet Kotto 11/15/44
Sandy Koufax 12/30/35
Ernie Kovaks 1/23/19
Julian Krainin 1/24/41
Jack Kramer 8/5/21

Larry Kramer 1/25/35
Stanley Kramer 9/23/13
Eric Krammer 11/6/64
Judith Krantz 1/9/28
Jerry Krause 4/6/39
Charles Krauthammer 3/13/50
Lenny Kravitz 5/26/64
Kreskin 1/12/35
Aaron Krickstein 8/2/67
Kris Kristofferson 6/22/37
Ray Kroc 10/5/02
Steve Kroft 8/22/45
Bernard Kroger 1/24/1860
Otto Kruger 9/6/1885
John Kruk 2/9/61
Jack Kruschen 3/20/22
Lee Kuan Yee 9/16/23
Tony Kubek 10/12/35
Stanley Kubrick 7/26/28
Bowie Kuhn 10/28/26
Maggie Kuhn 8/3/05
Toni Kukoc 9/18/68
Nancy Kulp 8/28/21
William Kunstler 7/7/19
Irv Kupcinet 7/31/12
Charles Kuralt 9/10/34
Akira Kurosawa 3/23/10
Bill Kurtis 9/21/40
Swoosie Kurtz 9/6/44
Harvey Kurtzman 10/3/24
Nancy Kwan 5/19/39

L

Patti Labelle 5/24/44
Catherine Lacoste 6/27/45
Rene Lacoste 7/2/05
Jerry Lacy 3/27/36
Alan Ladd 9/3/13
Alan Ladd, Jr. 10/22/37
Cheryl Ladd 7/12/52

Diane Ladd 11/29/32
Christian Laettner 8/17/69
Arthur Laffer 8/14/35
Guy Lafleur 9/20/51
Karl Lagerfeld 9/10/38
Bert Lahr 8/13/1895
Christine Lahti 4/5/50
Bill Laimbeer 5/19/57
Cleo Laine 10/28/27
Frankie Laine 3/30/13
R.D. Laing 10/7/27
Melvin Laird 9/1/22
Anthony Lake 4/2/63
Ricki Lake 9/21/68
Veronica Lake 11/14/19
Freddie Laker 8/6/22
Arthur Lakes 4/17/05
Jack LaLanne 9/26/14
Michael Lally 5/25/42
Barbara LaMarr 7/28/1896
Hedy Lamarr 11/9/14
Franando Lamas 1/9/20
Lorenzo Lamas 1/20/58
Brian Lamb 10/9/41
Daryle Lamonica 7/17/41
Jake LaMotta 7/10/21
Dorothy Lamour 12/10/14
Burt Lancaster 11/2/13
Elsa Lancaster 10/28/02
Bert Lance 6/3/31
Edwin Land 5/7/09
Ely Landau 1/20/20
Martin Landau 6/20/34
Ann Landers 7/4/18
Carole Landis 1/1/19
John Landis 8/3/50
Michael Landon 10/31/36
Greg Landry 12/18/46
Tom Landry 9/11/24
Abbe Lane 12/14/32
Burton Lane 2/2/12
Fritz Lang 12/5/1890
k.d. Lang 11/2/61
Harry Langdon 6/15/1884

Sue Ann Langdon 3/8/36
Hope Lange 11/28/38
Jessica Lange 4/20/49
Ted Lange 1/5/49
Frank Langella 1/1/40
Frances Langford 4/4/14
Bob Lanier 9/10/48
Lester Lanin 8/26/11
Angela Lansbury 10/16/25
Robert Lansing 6/5/29
Sherry Lansing 7/31/44
Meyer Lansky 7/4/02
Snooky Lanson 3/27/19
Walter Lantz 4/27/00
Barnard Lanvin 12/27/35
Mario Lanza 1/31/21
Ted Lapidus 6/23/29
Ring Lardner 3/3/1885
Ring Lardner, Jr. 8/19/15
Steve Largent 9/28/54
Barry Larkin 8/24/64
Julius LaRosa 1/2/30
John Larroquette 11/25/47
Gary Larson 8/14/50
Nicolette Larson 7/17/52
Tony Larussa 10/4/44
Jesse Lasky 9/13/1880
Victor Lasky 1/7/18
Tommy Lasorda 9/22/27
Louis Lasser 4/11/39
Sydney Lassick 7/23/22
Matt Lattanzi 2/1/59
Niki Lauda 2/22/49
Estee Lauder 7/1/08
Charles Laughton 7/1/1899
Cyndi Lauper 6/20/53
Stan Laurel 6/16/1890
Ralph Lauren 10/14/39
Arthur Laurents 7/14/18
Piper Laurie 1/22/32
Rod Laver 8/9/38
Linda Lavin 10/15/37
John Phillip Law 9/7/37
Peter Lawford 9/7/23

Lawrence of Arabia	8/15/1888
Carol Lawrence	9/5/32
D.H. Lawrence	9/11/1885
Steve Lawrence	7/8/35
Tracy Lawrence	1/27/68
Vicki Lawrence	3/26/49
Paul Laxalt	8/2/22
Bobby Layne	12/19/26
Joe Layton	5/3/31
Irving Lazar	3/28/07
Lash LaRue	5/3/02
Oliver LaFarge	12/19/01
Eva LaGallienne	1/11/1899
Fiorello LaGuadia	12/11/1882
Robin Leach	8/29/41
Cloris Leachman	4/30/30
Leadbelly	1/20/1888
Frank Leahy	8/27/08
Patrick Leahy	3/31/40
Richard Leakey	12/19/44
David Lean	3/25/08
Bill Lear	6/26/02
Norman Lear	7/27/22
Michael Learned	4/9/39
Timothy Leary	10/22/20
Christian Laettner	8/17/69
Fran Lebowitz	10/27/50
John LeCarre	10/19/31
Henri LeConte	7/4/63
Brenda Lee	12/11/44
Bruce Lee	11/27/40
Christopher Lee	5/27/22
Dixie Lee	11/4/11
Gypsy Rose Lee	1/9/14
Harper Lee	4/28/26
Michele Lee	6/24/42
Peggy Lee	5/26/20
Robert E. Lee	1/19/1807
Spike Lee	3/20/57
Tommy Lee	10/3/62
Sybil Leek	2/22/17
Michel Legrand	2/24/32
Ursula LeGuin	10/21/29
Franz Lehar	4/30/1870
Christopher Lehmann-Haupt	6/14/34
James Lehrer	5/19/34
Ron Leibman	10/11/37
Janet Leigh	7/6/27
Mike Leigh	2/20/43
Jennifer Jason Leigh	2/5/62
Vivien Leigh	11/5/13
Bert Leighton	12/29/1877
Margaret Leighton	2/26/22
Erich Leinsdorf	2/4/12
Donovan Leitch	5/10/46
Gen. Curtis LeMay	11/15/06
Harvey Lembeck	4/15/23
Mario Lemieux	10/5/65
Jack Lemmon	2/8/25
Bob Lemon	9/22/20
Meadowlark Lemon	4/25/32
Greg Lemond	6/26/61
Gene Lemont	12/25/46
Ivan Lendl	3/7/60
Nikolai Lenin	4/9/1870
Dianne Lennon	12/1/39
John Lennon	10/9/40
Julian Lennon	4/8/63
Sean Lennon	10/9/75
Annie Lennox	12/25/54
Jay Leno	4/28/50
Lotte Lenya	10/18/00
Kay Lenz	3/4/53
Elmore Leonard	10/11/25
Jack E. Leonard	4/24/11
Sheldon Leonard	2/22/07
Sugar Ray Leonard	5/17/56
Lawrence Leritz	9/26/52
Alan Jay Lerner	8/31/18
Max Lerner	12/20/02
Mervyn LeRoy	10/15/00
Joan Leslie	1/26/25
Doris Lessing	10/22/19
Richard Lester	1/19/32
David Letterman	4/12/47
Oscar LeVant	12/27/06
Sam Levenson	12/28/11
Eddie LeVert	6/16/42

Carl Levin 6/29/34	Charles Lindbergh 2/4/02
Ira Levin 8/27/29	Hal Linden 3/20/31
Irving R. Levine......................... 8/26/22	Cec Linder 3/10/21
James Levine............................... 6/23/43	Viveca Lindfors 12/29/20
Joseph Levine 9/9/05	John V. Lindsay 11/24/21
Meyer Levine............................. 10/6/05	Mort Lindsey 3/21/23
Cliff Levingston 1/4/61	Pia Lindstrom 9/20/38
Barry Levinson 4/6/32	Art Linkletter 7/17/12
Eugene Levy 12/17/46	Bambi Linn................................. 4/26/26
Marv Levy 8/3/29	Larry Linville............................. 9/29/39
Anthony Lewis 3/27/27	Ray Liotta 12/18/55
Carl Lewis 7/1/61	Louis Lipps 8/9/62
Emanuel Lewis 3/9/71	Peggy Lipton 8/30/47
Huey Lewis 7/5/51	Sonny Liston 5/8/32
Jerry Lewis 3/16/26	John Lithgow 10/19/45
Jerry Lee Lewis 9/29/35	Little Anthony 1/8/41
John Lewis 2/21/40	Cleavon Little 6/1/39
Juliette Lewis 6/21/73	Rich Little 11/26/38
Ramsey Lewis.............................. 5/27/35	Gene Littler 7/21/30
Reggie Lewis 11/21/65	Penelope Lively 3/17/33
Reginald Lewis 12/7/42	Roger Livesey 6/25/06
Richard Lewis............................ 6/29/47	Jay Livingston............................ 3/29/15
Shari Lewis 1/17/34	Christopher Lloyd 10/22/38
Sinclair Lewis 2/7/1885	David Lloyd 1/3/48
Ted Lewis............................... 10/24/1894	Harold Lloyd 4/20/1893
Simon Le Bon.......................... 10/27/58	John Lloyd.................................. 8/27/54
Liberace 5/16/19	Meat Loaf 9/27/47
Roy Lichtenstein 10/27/23	John Locke 8/29/1632
G. Gordon Liddy..................... 11/30/30	Sandra Locke 5/28/47
Trygve Lie 7/16/1896	Gene Lockhart 7/18/1891
Joseph Lieberman 2/24/42	June Lockhart 6/25/25
Judith Light................................ 2/9/50	Heather Locklear 9/25/61
Gordon Lightfoot 11/17/38	Gary Lockwood 2/21/37
Beatrice Lillie 5/29/1898	Margaret Lockwood 9/15/16
Doris Lilly 12/26/26	Barbara Loden 7/8/37
Arthur Liman 11/5/32	Henry Cabot Lodge 7/5/02
Rush Limbaugh 1/12/51	Frank Loesser 6/29/10
Limmahl 12/19/58	James Lofton 7/5/56
Maya Lin 10/5/59	Joshua Logan 10/5/08
Abbey Lincoln 8/6/30	Robert Loggia 1/3/30
Abraham Lincoln 2/12/1809	Kenny Loggins 1/7/48
Mary Todd Lincoln............. 12/13/1818	Gina Lollobrigida 7/4/28
Robert Todd Lincoln 8/1/1843	Carol Lombard 10/6/09
Anne Morrow Lindbergh 6/22/06	Vince Lombardi......................... 6/11/13

Guy Lombardo 6/19/02	Rob Lowe 3/17/64
Jack London 1/12/1876	Malcolm Lowry 7/28/09
Julie London 9/26/26	Myrna Loy 8/2/05
Earl Long 8/26/1895	George Lucas 5/14/44
Huey P. Long 8/30/1893	Susan Lucci 12/23/46
Shelley Long 8/23/49	Clare Boothe Luce 4/10/03
Claudine Longet 1/29/42	Henry Luce 4/3/1898
Anita Loos 4/26/1893	Lucky Luciano 11/24/1897
Davey Lopes 5/3/45	Laurence Luckingbill 11/21/34
Nancy Lopez 1/6/57	Charles Ludlam 4/12/43
Priscilla Lopez 2/26/48	Robert Ludlum 5/25/27
Trini Lopez 5/15/37	Richard Lugar 4/4/32
Federico Garcia Lorca 6/5/1899	Bela Lugosi 10/20/1882
Jack Lord 12/30/30	Johnny Lujack 1/4/25
Traci Lords 5/7/68	Paul Lukas 5/26/1894
Sophia Loren 9/20/34	Keye Luke 6/18/04
Frank Lorenzo 5/19/40	Sidney Lumet 6/25/24
Gloria Loring 12/10/46	Jimmy Lunceford 6/6/02
Peter Lorre 6/26/04	Joan Lunden 9/19/51
Victoria De Los Angeles 11/1/24	Dolph Lundgren 10/17/59
Ronnie Lott 5/8/59	William Lundigan 6/12/14
Trent Lott 10/9/41	David Lundstrom 6/7/47
John D. Loudermilk 3/31/34	Alfred Lunt 8/19/1892
Dorothy Loudon 9/17/33	Ida Lupino 2/4/18
Greg Louganis 1/29/60	Patti Lupone 4/21/49
Kevin Loughery 3/4/40	Alison Lurie 9/3/26
Mary Loughlin 6/30/56	Martin Luther 11/10/1483
Joe Louis 5/13/14	Richard Lutz 2/12/32
Julia Louis-Dreyfus 1/13/61	David Lynch 1/20/46
Marie Louise 12/12/1791	Paul Lynde 6/13/26
Tina Louise 2/11/37	Carol Lynley 2/13/43
Jack Lousma 2/29/30	Diana Lynn 10/7/26
Bessie Love 9/10/1898	Fred Lynn 2/3/52
Davis Love III 4/13/64	Janet Lynn 4/6/53
Mike Love 3/15/41	Loretta Lynn 4/14/35
H.P. Lovecraft 8/20/1890	Jeff Lynne 12/30/42
Clarence Lovejoy 6/26/1894	Sue Lyon 7/10/46
Frank Lovejoy 3/28/14	
Patty Loveless 1/4/57	
James Lovell 3/25/23	
Lyle Lovett 11/1/57	
Jon Lovitz 7/21/57	
Juliette Gorden Low 10/31/1860	
Frederick Lowe 6/10/04	

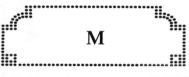

Yo Yo Ma 10/7/55

Lorin Maazel 3/5/30	Taj Mahal 5/17/42
Moms Mabley 3/19/1894	George Maharis 9/1/33
Arthur MacArthur 6/2/1845	John Mahoney 6/20/40
Douglas MacArthur 1/26/1880	Rick Mahorn 9/21/58
James MacArthur 12/8/37	Phil Mahre 5/10/57
Ralph Macchio 11/4/62	Steve Mahre 5/10/57
Jeanette MacDonald 6/18/01	Norman Mailer 1/31/23
John MacDonald 7/24/16	Majorie Main 2/24/1890
Andie MacDowell 4/21/58	Dan Majerle 9/9/65
Spanky MacFarland 10/2/28	John Major 3/29/43
Jack MacGowran 10/13/18	Lee Majors 4/23/40
Ali MacGraw 4/1/38	Natalia Makarova 11/21/40
Connie Mack 10/29/40	Miriam Makeba 3/4/32
Connie Mack (Baseball) 12/22/1862	Bernard Malamud 4/26/16
Kevin Mack 8/9/62	Karl Malden 3/22/13
Ted Mack 2/12/04	Magdalena Maleeva 4/1/75
Gisele Mackenzie 1/10/27	Judith Malina 6/4/26
Bob Mackie 3/24/40	Bronislaw Malinowski 4/6/1884
Janet MacLachian 2/27/46	John Malkovich 12/9/53
Kyle MacLachlan 2/22/59	Louis Malle 10/30/32
Shirley MacLaine 4/24/34	Dorothy Malone 1/30/25
Barton MacLane 12/25/02	Jeff Malone 6/28/61
Archibald MacLeish 5/7/1892	Karl Malone 7/24/63
Gavin MacLeod 2/28/30	Moses Malone 3/23/55
John MacLeod 10/3/37	Andre Malraux 11/3/01
Fred MacMurray 8/30/08	Leonard Maltin 12/18/50
Patrick MacNee 2/6/22	David Mamet 11/30/45
Robert MacNeil 1/19/31	Melisse Manchester 2/15/51
Jeffrey MacNelly 9/17/47	William Manchester 4/4/22
Uncle Dave Macon 10/7/1870	Henry Mancini 4/16/24
Gordon MacRae 3/12/21	Ray "Boom Boom" Mancini 3/4/61
Meredith MacRae 5/30/44	Robert Mandan 2/2/32
Sheila MacRae 9/24/24	Nelson Mandela 7/18/18
George Macready 8/29/09	Howie Mandell 11/29/55
John Madden 4/10/36	Og Mandino 12/12/23
Greg Maddux 4/14/66	Hana Mandlikova 2/19/62
Lester Maddox 9/30/15	Barbara Mandrell 12/25/48
Guy Madison 1/19/22	Edouard Manet 1/23/1832
Madonna 8/16/58	Silvava Mangano 4/21/30
Ira C. Magaziner 11/8/47	Chuck Mangione 11/29/40
Anna Magnani 3/7/09	Barry Manilow 6/17/46
Rene Magritte 11/21/1898	Joseph Mankiewicz 2/11/09
Jeb Stuart Magruder 11/5/34	Dexter Manley 2/2/59
John Mahaffey 5/9/48	Charles Mann 4/12/61

Delbert Mann 1/30/20
Manfred Mann 10/21/40
Thomas Mann 6/6/1875
Archie Manning 5/19/49
Danny Manning 5/17/66
Jayne Mansfield 4/19/32
Charles Manson 11/11/34
Joe Mantegna 11/13/47
Mickey Mantle 10/20/31
Randolph Mantooth 9/19/44
Marla Maples-Trump 10/26/63
Jean Paul Marat 5/24/1743
Pete Maravich 6/22/48
Marcel Marceau 3/22/23
Fredric March 8/31/1897
Nancy Marchand 6/19/28
Ted Marchibroda 3/15/31
Rocky Marciano 9/1/23
Ferdinand Marcos 9/11/17
Princess Margaret 8/21/30
Juan Marichal 10/24/37
Ed Marinaro 3/3/50
Dan Marino 9/15/61
Roger Maris 9/10/34
Johnny Marks 10/10/09
Bob Marley 5/5/45
Hugh Marlowe 1/30/14
J.P. Marquand 11/10/1893
Gabriel Garcia Marquez 3/6/28
David Marr 12/27/33
John W. Marriott 9/17/00
Bradford Marsalis 8/26/60
Wynton Marsalis 10/18/61
Jean Marsh 7/1/34
Mae Marsh 11/9/1895
E.G. Marshall 6/18/10
Garry Marshall 11/13/34
George C. Marshall 12/31/1880
Henry Marshall 8/9/54
Penny Marshall 10/15/45
Peter Marshall 3/30/30
Thurgood Marshall 7/2/08
Wilber Marshall 4/18/62
Peter Marten 10/27/46

Billy Martin 5/16/28
Dean Martin 6/7/17
Dick Martin 1/30/32
Judith Martin 9/13/38
Mary Martin 12/1/14
Pamela Sue Martin 1/5/54
Steve Martin 8/14/45
Tony Martin 12/25/13
Al Martinez 6/21/29
Edgar Martinez 1/2/63
Al Martino 11/7/27
Peter Martins 10/11/46
Lee Marvin 2/19/24
Chico Marx 3/22/1891
Groucho Marx 10/2/1890
Harpo Marx 11/23/1893
Karl Marx 5/5/1818
Zeppo Marx 2/25/01
Mary, Queen of Scots 12/7/1542
Masaccio 12/21/1401
Hugh Masekela 4/4/39
Giulietta Masina 3/22/21
Jamal Mashburn 11/29/72
Abraham Maslow 4/1/08
Anthony Mason 12/14/66
Dave Mason 5/10/46
Jackie Mason 6/9/30
James Mason 5/15/09
Marsha Mason 4/3/42
Pamela Mason 3/10/22
Ilona Massey 6/16/10
Raymond Massey 8/30/1896
Dr. William Masters 12/27/15
Edgar Lee Masters 8/22/1869
Virgina Masters 2/11/25
Bat Masterson 11/24/1853
Peter Masterson 6/1/34
Mary Elizabeth Mastrantonio 11/17/58
Marcello Mastroianni 9/28/24
Kurt Masur 7/18/27
Jerry Mathers 6/2/48
Tim Matheson 12/31/48
Carmen Mathews 5/8/18
Johnny Mathis 9/30/35

Henri Matisse	12/31/1869	Doug McClure	5/11/35
Marlee Matlin	8/24/65	Marilyn McCoo	9/30/44
Robert Matsui	9/17/47	Patty McCormick	8/21/45
Kathy Mattea	6/21/59	Willie McCovey	1/10/38
Walter Matthau	10/1/20	Alec McCowen	5/26/26
Don Mattingly	4/20/61	Tim McCoy	4/10/1891
Victor Mature	1/29/16	Joel McCrea	11/5/06
Gene Mauch	11/18/25	Carson McCullers	2/19/17
Somerset Maugham	1/25/1874	Hattie McDaniel	6/10/1895
Bill Mauldin	10/29/21	Mel McDaniel	9/6/42
Andre Maurois	7/26/1885	Xavier McDaniel	6/4/63
Peter Max	10/19/37	Alice McDermott	6/27/53
Frank Maxwell	11/17/16	Jim McDivitt	6/10/29
Marilyn Maxwell	8/3/21	James McDonnell	4/9/1899
Elaine May	4/21/32	Malcolm McDowell	6/19/43
Rollo May	4/21/09	Roddy McDowell	9/17/28
Louis B. Mayer	7/4/1885	John McEnroe	2/16/59
Curtis Mayfield	6/3/42	Reba McEntire	3/28/55
Ken Maynard	6/21/1895	Mary McFadden	10/1/38
Robert Maynard	6/17/37	Bobby McFerrin	3/11/50
Virginia Mayo	11/30/20	Darren McGavin	5/7/22
Melanie Mayron	10/20/52	Fibber McGee	11/16/1896
Willie Mays	5/6/31	Willie McGee	11/2/58
Mike Mazurki	12/24/09	Kelly McGillis	7/9/57
Paul Mazursky	4/25/30	Ted McGinley	5/30/58
Bob McAdoo	9/25/51	John McGiver	11/5/13
Martina McBride	7/29/66	Patrick McGoohan	3/19/28
David McCallum	9/19/33	Elizabeth McGovern	7/18/61
Napoleon McCallum	10/6/63	George McGovern	7/19/22
Mercedes McCambride	3/17/18	Maureen McGovern	7/27/49
Leo McCarey	10/3/1898	Tug McGraw	8/30/44
Eugene McCarthy	3/29/16	Fred McGriff	10/31/63
J.P. McCarthy	3/22/34	Dorothy McGuire	6/14/18
Kevin McCarthy	2/15/14	Kevin McHale	12/19/57
Mary McCarthy	6/21/12	Jay McInerney	1/13/55
Linda McCartney	9/24/42	John McIntire	6/27/07
Paul McCartney	6/18/42	Reba McIntire	3/29/55
Jim McCarty	7/25/43	Jim McKay	9/24/21
Tim McCarver	10/16/41	John McKay	7/5/23
Michael McCaskey	12/11/43	Ian McKellen	5/25/39
Rue McClanahan	2/21/34	Siobhan McKenna	5/24/22
George B. McClellan	12/3/1826	Reggie McKenzie	7/27/56
Guthrie McClintic	8/6/1893	Nancy McKeon	4/4/66
Paul McCloskey	9/29/27	Phillip McKeon	11/11/64

Leo McKern 3/16/20	Andrew Mellon 3/24/1855
Ron McKernan 9/8/46	Paul Mellon 6/11/07
Dennis McKinnon 8/22/61	Daniel Melnick 4/21/32
Rod McKuen 4/29/33	Herman Melville 8/1/1819
Victor McLaglen 12/11/1886	Harold Melvin 5/24/41
Denny McLain 3/29/44	H.L. Mencken 9/12/1880
John McLaughlin 3/29/27	Sergio Mendes 2/11/41
Don McLean 10/2/45	Chris Menge 9/15/40
Marshall McLuhan 7/21/11	Josef Mengele 2/7/11
Ed McMahon 3/6/23	Adolphe Menjou 2/8/1890
Jim McMahon 8/21/59	Karl Menninger 7/23/1893
Tom McMillens 5/26/52	William Menninger 10/15/1899
Larry McMurtry 6/3/36	Gian Carlo Menotti 7/7/11
Barbara McNair 3/4/37	Yehudi Menuhin 4/22/16
Terrace McNally 11/3/39	Johnny Mercer 11/18/09
Robert McNamara 6/9/16	Marian Mercer 11/26/35
Scott McNealy 11/13/54	Ismail Merchant 12/25/36
James McNichol 7/2/61	Vivien Merchant 7/22/29
Kristy McNichol 9/9/62	Melina Mercouri 10/18/25
Aimee Semple McPherson .. 10/9/1890	Freddie Mercury 9/8/46
Butterfly McQueen 1/8/11	Burgess Meredith 11/16/08
Steve McQueen 3/24/30	Don Meredith 4/10/38
Carmen McRae 4/8/22	James Meredith 6/25/33
Hal McRae 7/10/45	Lee Ann Meriwether 5/27/35
Gerald McRaney 8/19/48	Una Merkel 12/10/03
Christie McVie 7/12/43	Ethel Merman 1/16/09
John McVie 11/25/45	David Merrick 11/27/12
Norris McWhirter 8/12/25	Dina Merrill 12/9/25
Ross McWhirter 8/12/25	Gray Merrill 8/2/15
Margaret Mead 12/16/01	Robert Merrill 6/4/19
Jayne Meadows 9/27/26	Mark Messier 1/18/61
George Meany 8/16/1894	Grace Metalious 9/8/24
Anne Meara 9/20/29	Pat Metheny 8/12/54
Rick Mears 12/3/51	Howard Metzenbaum 6/4/17
Meat Loaf 9/27/48	Ray Meyer 12/18/13
Evan Mecham 3/12/24	Kweisi Mfume 10/24/48
Catherine de Medici 4/13/1519	George Michael 6/25/63
Ralph Meeker 11/21/20	Michelangelo 3/5/1475
Zubin Mehta 4/29/36	Al Michaels 11/12/44
Golda Meir 5/3/1898	Edouard Michelin 6/23/1859
Eddie Mekka 6/14/52	James Michener 2/3/07
Nellie Melba 5/19/1859	Bette Midler 12/1/45
Lauritz Melchior 3/20/1890	Toshiro Mifune 4/1/20
John Cougar Mellcamp 10/7/51	Alyssa Milano 12/19/73

Buddy Miles	9/5/46	Carmen Miranda	2/9/09
JoAnna Miles	3/6/40	Rick Mirer	3/3/70
Sarah Miles	12/31/43	Walter Mirisch	11/8/21
Sylvia Miles	9/9/32	Joan Miro	4/20/1893
Vera Miles	8/23/29	Arthur Mitchell	3/27/34
John Milius	4/11/44	Cameron Mitchell	11/18/18
Ray Milland	1/3/08	Chad Mitchell	12/5/36
Edna St. Vincent Millay	2/22/1892	George Mitchell	8/20/33
Ann Miller	4/12/23	Guy Mitchell	2/21/27
Arthur Miller	10/17/15	John Mitchell	9/5/13
Dennis Miller	11/3/54	Joni Mitchell	11/7/43
Glenn Miller	3/1/04	Margaret Mitchell	11/8/00
Henry Miller	12/26/1891	Martha Mitchell	9/2/18
Jason Miller	4/22/39	Scoey Mitchell	3/12/30
Jeremy Miller	10/21/76	Scott Mitchell	1/2/68
Johnny Miller	4/29/47	Thomas Mitchell	7/10/1892
Jonathan Miller	7/21/34	Marvin Mitchlson	5/7/28
Mitch Miller	7/4/11	Robert Mitchum	8/6/17
Nicole Miller	3/20/51	Francois Mitterrand	10/26/16
Penelope Ann Miller	1/13/64	Tom Mix	1/6/1880
Reggie Miller	8/24/65	Mary Ann Mobley	2/17/39
Roger Miller	1/2/36	Dottie Mochrie	8/17/70
Steve Miller	10/5/43	Art Modell	6/23/25
Spike Milligan	4/16/18	Amadeo Modigliani	7/12/1884
Chris Mills	1/25/70	Matthew Modine	3/22/59
Donna Mills	12/11/43	Doug Moe	9/21/38
Hayley Mills	4/18/46	Donald Moffat	12/26/30
Sir John Mills	2/22/08	Katy Moffatt	11/19/50
Stephanie Mills	3/22/57	Anna Moffo	6/27/34
Terry Mills	12/21/67	Moliere	1/15/1622
Wilburn Mills	5/24/09	Paul Molitor	8/22/56
Martin Milner	12/28/27	Tom Monaghan	3/25/37
Sherrill Milnes	1/10/35	Sidney Moncrief	9/21/57
Czeslaw Milosz	6/29/11	Joan Mondale	8/8/30
Ronnie Milsap	1/16/44	Walter Mondale	1/5/28
Nathan Milstein	12/31/04	Claude Monet	11/14/1840
John Milton	12/9/1608	Art Monk	12/5/57
Yvette Mimieux	1/8/41	Thelonious Monk	10/10/20
Piero Mimitri	7/1/33	Earl Monroe	11/21/44
Sal Mineo	1/10/39	Marilyn Monroe	6/1/26
Charles Mingus	4/22/22	Vaughn Monroe	10/7/11
Ho Chi Minh	5/19/1890	Nicholas Monsarrat	3/22/10
Liza Minnelli	3/12/46	Ashley Montagu	6/28/05
Vincente Minnelli	2/28/13	Ricardo Montalban	11/25/20

Bob Montana 10/23/20
Claude Montana 6/29/49
Joe Montana 6/11/56
Yves Montand 10/13/21
Maria Montessori 8/31/1870
Belinda Montgomery 7/23/50
Carlos Montgomery 12/13/03
Elizabeth Montgomery 4/15/33
George Montgomery 8/29/16
Robert Montgomery 5/21/04
Carlos Montoya 12/13/03
Rev. Sun Myung Moon 1/6/20
Warren Moon 11/18/56
Archie Moore 12/13/13
Clayton Moore 9/14/14
Colleen Moore 8/19/02
Demi Moore 11/11/62
Dickie Moore 9/12/25
Dudley Moore 4/19/35
Gary Moore 1/13/15
Mary Tyler Moore 12/29/37
Melba Moore 10/29/45
Nat Moore 9/19/51
Roger Moore 10/14/27
Sam Moore 10/12/35
Terry Moore 1/1/32
Agnes Moorehead 12/6/06
James Mora 5/24/35
Erin Moran 10/18/61
Rick Moranis 4/18/54
Alberto Moravia 11/28/07
Jeanne Moreau 1/23/28
Rita Moreno 12/11/31
Dennis Morgan 12/30/20
Frank Morgan 6/1/1890
Harry Morgan 4/10/15
Helen Morgan 8/2/00
Henry Morgan 3/31/15
J.P. Morgan 4/17/1837
Joe Morgan (Baseball Player) .. 9/19/43
Lorrie Morgan 6/6/59
Michele Morgan 2/29/20
Michael Moriarty 4/5/42
Pat Morita 6/28/33

Christopher Morley 5/5/1890
Robert Morley 5/26/08
Chester Morris 2/16/01
Desmond Morris 1/24/28
Eugene "Mercury" Morris 1/5/47
Garrett Morris 2/1/37
Greg Morris 9/27/34
Jack Morris 5/16/55
Jan Morris 10/21/26
Wayne Morris 2/17/14
Willie Morris 11/29/34
William Morris, Jr. 10/22/1899
Jim Morrison 12/8/43
Shelly Morrison 10/26/36
Toni Morrison 2/18/31
Van Morrison 8/31/45
Karen Morrow 12/15/36
Vic Morrow 2/14/32
Barry Morse 6/10/18
Robert Morse 5/18/31
Jelly Roll Morton 9/20/1885
Willie Mosconi 6/21/13
Mark Moseley 3/12/48
Carol Moseley-Braun 8/16/47
Billy R. Moses 1/17/59
Grandma Moses 9/7/1860
Cynthia Moss 7/24/40
Geoffrey Moss 6/30/38
Kate Moss 1/16/74
Stirling Moss 9/17/29
Donny Most 8/8/53
Zero Mostel 2/28/15
Manny Mota 2/18/38
Alonzo Mourning 2/8/70
Alan Mowbray 8/18/1896
Bill Moyers 6/5/34
Daniel Moynihan 3/16/27
Leopold Mozart................... 11/14/1719
Wolfgang Amadeus Mozart 1/27/1756
Hosni Mubarak 5/4/28
Roger Mudd................................ 2/9/28
Robert Mugabe 2/21/24
Malcolm Muggeridge............... 3/24/03
Elijah Muhammad 10/7/1897

Fard Muhammad 2/26/1877
Wallace Muhammad 10/30/33
Bharati Mukherjee 7/27/40
Diana Muldaur 8/19/38
Maria Muldaur 9/12/43
Kate Mulgrew 4/29/55
Edward Mulhare 4/8/47
Martin Mull 8/18/43
Gerry Mulligan......................... 4/5/27
Richard Mulligan 11/13/32
Chris Mullin............................. 7/30/63
Brian Mulroney 3/20/39
Paul Muni 9/22/1895
Anthony Munoz 8/19/58
Patrice Munsel 5/14/26
Thurman Munson 6/7/47
Iris Murdoch 7/15/19
Rupert Murdoch 3/11/31
Audie Murphy 6/20/24
Ben Murphy............................... 3/6/42
Dale Murphy 3/12/56
Eddie Murphy 4/3/61
Michael Murphy 5/5/38
Anne Murray 6/20/45
Arthur Murray 4/4/1895
Bill Murray 9/21/50
Don Murray 7/31/29
Eddie Murray 2/24/56
Jan Murray 10/4/17
Patty Murray 10/11/50
Edward R. Murrow 4/25/08
Brent Musburger 5/26/39
Stan Musial 11/21/20
Ed Muskie 3/28/14
Benito Mussolini 7/29/1883
M.P. Mussorgsky 3/21/1839
Riccardo Muti 7/28/41
Dikembe Mutombo 6/25/66
Dee Dee Myers 9/1/61
Pete Myers 9/15/63
Russell Myers 10/9/38
Alan Myerson 8/8/36
Bess Myerson........................... 7/16/24

N

Vladimir Nabokov 4/23/1899
Jim Nabors 6/12/32
Michael Nader 2/18/45
Ralph Nader 2/27/34
Conrad Nagel 3/16/1897
J. Carrol Naish 1/21/00
James Naismith 11/6/1861
Nita Naldi 4/1/1899
Joe Namath 5/31/43
Larry Nance 2/12/59
Graham Nash 2/2/42
Johnny Nash 8/19/40
Ogden Nash 8/19/02
Conde Nast 3/26/1874
Ilie Nastase.............................. 7/19/49
Carry Nation........................ 11/24/1846
Mildred Natwick...................... 6/19/08
David Naughton 2/13/51
James Naughton........................ 12/6/45
Victor Navasky........................... 7/5/32
Martina Navatilova 10/18/56
Gloria Naylor............................ 1/25/50
Youssou Ndour 10/1/59
Patricia Neal 1/20/26
Ronald Neame........................... 4/23/11
Lynn Neary 1/31/50
Hal Needham 3/6/31
Liam Neeson 6/7/52
Hildegarde Neff 12/28/25
Pola Negri 12/31/1894
Jean Negulesco 2/29/00
Jawaharlal Nehru 11/14/1889
Leroy Neiman............................. 6/8/26
Kate Nelligan 3/16/51
Barry Nelson 4/16/20
Craig T. Nelson 4/4/46
David Nelson........................... 10/24/36
Don Nelson 5/15/40

Ed Nelson 12/21/28	Stevie Nicks 5/26/48
Gene Nelson 3/24/20	Jean Nidetch 10/12/23
Harriet Nelson 7/18/12	Reinhold Niebuhr 6/21/1892
Judd Nelson 11/28/59	Joe Niekro 11/7/44
Lindsey Nelson 5/25/19	Arthur C. Nielsen 9/5/1897
Lori Nelson 8/15/33	Brigitte Nielsen........................... 7/17/63
Ozzie Nelson 3/20/06	Carl August Nielsen 6/9/1865
Ricky Nelson 5/8/40	Leslie Nielsen 2/11/26
Tracy Nelson.............................. 12/27/44	Friedrich Nietzsche............. 10/15/1844
Willie Nelson 4/30/33	Florence Nightingale 5/12/1820
Nero .... 12/15/37 AD	Vaslav Nijinsky 2/28/1890
Peter Nero 5/22/34	Brigit Nilsson............................. 5/17/18
Pablo Neruda............................. 7/12/04	Harry Nilsson 6/15/41
Cathleen Nesbitt 11/24/1889	Leonard Nimoy 3/26/31
Michael Nesmith 12/30/42	Anais Nin 2/21/03
Eliot Ness 4/19/03	Ray Nitschke............................. 12/29/36
Al Neuharth 3/22/24	David Niven 3/1/10
John Neville 5/2/25	Marni Nixon 2/22/30
Chuck Nevitt 6/13/59	Norm Nixon 10/11/55
Don Newcombe 6/14/26	Patricia Nixon............................ 3/16/12
Bob Newhart............................... 9/5/29	Richard Nixon 1/9/13
S.I. Newhouse......................... 5/24/1895	Julie Nixon-Eisenhower 7/5/48
Hal Newhouser 5/20/21	Tricia Nixon-Cox....................... 2/21/46
Anthony Newley 9/24/31	Louis Nizer 2/6/02
Barry Newman 11/7/38	Yannick Noah.............................. 5/16/60
David Newman 2/24/32	Alfred Bernhard Nobel 10/21/1833
Edwin Newman 1/25/19	James Nobel 3/5/22
Laraine Newman 3/2/52	Chelsea Noble............................ 12/4/64
Paul Newman............................. 1/26/25	Lyn Nofziger 6/8/24
Phyllis Newman 3/19/35	Isamu Noguchi 11/4/04
Randy Newman 11/28/43	Jeannette Nolan 12/30/11
Julie Newmar 8/16/35	Kathleen Nolan 9/27/33
Tommy Newsom 2/25/29	Lloyd Noland 8/11/02
Ozzie Newson 3/16/56	Chuck Noll 1/5/31
Huey P. Newton 2/17/42	Nick Nolte..................................... 2/8/42
Sir Isaac Newton 1/4/1643	Hideo Nomo 8/31/68
Nate Newton 12/20/61	Peggy Noonan 9/7/50
Wayne Newton 4/3/42	Peter Noone 11/5/47
Olivia Newton-John 9/26/48	Greg Norman 2/10/55
Stavros Niarchos 7/3/09	Jessye Norman 9/15/45
Fayard Antonio Nichlas......... 10/20/14	Mabel Normand.................. 11/10/1897
Mike Nichols 11/6/31	Chuck Norris 3/10/40
Jack Nicholson........................... 4/22/37	Alex North 12/4/10
Jack Nicklaus 1/21/40	Jay North 8/3/52

Oliver North 10/7/43
Sheree North 1/17/33
Eleanor Holmes Norton 6/13/37
Ken Norton 8/9/45
Ken Norton, Jr. 9/29/66
Deborah Norville 8/8/58
Michael Nouri 12/9/46
Jay Novacek 10/24/62
Kim Novak.................................. 2/13/33
Robert Novak 2/26/31
Ramon Novarro 2/6/1899
Don Novello 1/1/43
Chris Novoselic 5/10/65
Jana Novotna 10/2/68
Ted Nugent 12/13/49
Sam Nunn 9/8/38
Rudolf Nureyev 3/17/38
France Nvyen 7/31/39
Diana Nyad................................ 8/22/49
Laura Nyro 10/18/47

O

Hugh O'Brian 4/19/30
Conan O'Brien 4/18/63
Edmund O'Brien 9/10/15
Lawrence O'Brien 7/7/17
Pat O'Brien........................... 11/11/1899
Margaret O'Brien 1/15/37
Sean O'Casey 3/30/1880
Arthur O'Connell...................... 3/29/08
Helen O'Connell 5/23/21
Edwin O'Connon 7/29/18
Cardinal John O'Connor 1/15/20
Flannery O'Connor 3/25/25
Sandra Day O'Connor 3/26/30
Carroll O'Connor 8/2/24
Donald O'Connor 8/30/25
Sinead O'Connor 12/8/66
Anita O'Day 10/18/18
Chris O'Donnell 6/26/70

Neil O'Donnell 7/3/66
Sean O'Faolain 2/22/00
Madalyn Murray O'Hair 3/13/19
Catherine O'Hara 3/4/54
John O'Hara 1/31/05
Maureen O'Hara 8/17/21
Dan O'Herlihy 5/2/19
Dennis O'Keefe 3/28/10
George O'Keeffee 11/15/1887
Pete O'Malley 12/12/37
Patrick O'Neal 9/26/27
Ryan O'Neal 4/20/41
Shaquille O'Neal 3/6/72
Tatum O'Neal........................... 11/5/63
Jennifer O'Neil 2/20/49
Ed O'Neill 4/12/46
Eugene O'Neill 10/16/1888
Tip O'Neill 12/9/12
Milo O'Shea 6/2/26
Maureen O'Sullian 5/17/11
Gilbert O'Sullivan 12/1/46
Annette O'Toole 4/1/53
Peter O'Toole 8/2/33
Jackie Oakie 11/12/03
Annie Oakley 8/13/1860
Charles Oakley 12/18/63
John Oates 4/7/49
Johnny Oates 1/21/46
Joyce Carol Oates 6/16/38
Merle Oberon 2/19/11
Ric Ocasek 3/23/49
Clifford Odet 7/18/06
Odetta 12/31/30
Jacques Offenbach 6/20/1819
Anne Sofiv Offer 5/9/55
Christian Okoye 8/16/61
Akeem Abdul Olajuwon 1/21/64
Warner Oland 10/3/1880
Claes Oldenburg 1/28/29
Gary Oldman............................. 3/21/58
Ransom Eli Olds..................... 6/3/1864
Ken Olin 7/30/55
Lena Olin 3/22/55
Patrick Oliphant 7/24/35

Lord Laurence Olivier 5/22/07
Edward James Olmos 2/24/47
Merlin Olsen 9/15/40
Aristotle Onassis 1/20/06
Christina Onassis 12/11/50
Jacqueline Onassis 7/28/29
Yoko Ono 2/18/33
Michael Ontkean 1/24/50
Marcel Ophuls 11/1/27
Max Ophuls 5/6/02
Jerry Orbach 10/20/35
Roy Orbison 4/23/36
Tony Orlando 4/3/44
Eugene Ormandy 11/18/1889
Bobby Orr 3/20/48
Brain Orser 12/18/61
George Orwell 6/25/03
John Osborne 3/15/07
Tom Osborne 2/23/37
Jeffrey Osbourne 3/9/48
Ozzy Osbourne 12/3/48
Oscar 3/29/1859
Charles Osgood 1/8/33
Donny Osmond 12/9/57
Jay Osmond 3/2/55
Marie Osmond 10/13/59
Lee Harvey Oswald 10/18/39
Merlene Ottey 5/10/60
Maria Ouspenskaya 7/29/1876
Park Overall 3/15/57
Michael Ovitz 12/14/46
Randy Owen 12/13/49
Billy Owens 5/1/69
Buck Owens 8/12/29
Gary Owens 5/10/35
Jesse Owens 9/12/13
Catherine Oxenberg 9/22/61
Frank Oz 5/24/44
Seiji Ozawa 9/1/35

P

Jack Paar 5/1/18
Frederick Pabst 3/28/1836
Al Pacino 4/25/40
Bob Packwood 9/11/32
Ignace Paderewski 11/18/1860
Clarence Page 6/2/47
Geraldine Page 11/22/24
Patti Page 11/8/27
Debra Paget 8/19/33
Camille Paglia 4/2/47
Reza Pahlavi 10/31/60
Shah Reza Pahlavi 10/26/19
Janis Paige 9/16/22
Satchel Paige 7/7/06
Harold Painter 10/10/30
Alan Pakula 4/7/28
Holly Palance 8/5/50
Jack Palance 2/18/20
William Paley 9/28/01
Ron Palillo 4/2/54
Michael Palin 5/5/43
Arnold Palmer 9/10/29
Betsy Palmer 11/1/26
Greg Palmer 1/25/27
Jim Palmer 10/15/45
Lilli Palmer 5/24/14
Robert Palmer 1/19/49
Eddie Palmieri 12/15/36
Leon Panetta 6/28/38
Franklin Pangborn 1/23/1893
Irene Papas 9/3/26
Joseph Papp 6/22/21
Bill Parcells 8/22/41
Michael Pare 10/4/59
Sara Paretsky 6/8/47
Robert Parish 8/30/53
Alan Parker 2/14/44
Brant Parker 8/26/20

Camilla Parker-Bowles............ 7/17/47	Tom Paxton............................. 10/31/37
Charlie Parker 8/29/20	Johnny Paycheck....................... 5/31/41
Dave Parker 6/9/51	Freda Payne 9/19/45
Dorothy Parker...................... 8/22/1893	John Payne 5/23/12
Eleanor Parker 6/26/22	John Howard Payne 6/9/1791
Fess Parker 8/16/27	Amanda Pays 6/6/59
Jameson Parker 11/18/48	Walter Payton 7/25/54
Jean Parker 8/11/12	Norman Vincent Peale 5/31/1898
Robert Brown Parker 9/17/32	Minnie Pearl 10/25/12
Sarah Jessica Parker 3/25/65	Drew Pearson 12/13/1897
Suzy Parker 10/28/33	Robert E. Peary 5/6/1856
Barbara Parkins 5/22/42	Gregory Peck 4/5/16
Bert Parks 12/30/14	Sam Peckinpah 2/21/25
Gordon Parks 11/30/12	Jan Peerce 6/3/04
Larry Parks 12/13/14	Calvin Peete 7/18/43
Rosa Parks................................... 2/4/13	Rodney Peete 3/16/66
Mollie Parnis............................. 3/18/05	I.M. Pei...................................... 4/26/17
Ara Parseghian 5/21/23	Pele.. 10/23/40
Estelle Parsons......................... 11/20/27	Clairborne Pell........................ 11/22/18
Arvo Part.................................... 9/11/35	Federico Pena 3/15/47
Dolly Parton.............................. 1/19/46	Tony Pena 6/4/57
Pier Paolo Pasolini 3/5/22	Teddy Pendergrass 3/26/50
John Dos Passos 1/14/1896	Terry Pendleton 7/16/60
Boris Pasternak...................... 2/11/1890	Arthur Penhallon 12/27/52
Joseph Pasternak 9/19/01	Arthur Penn 9/27/22
Louis Pasteur 12/27/1822	Irving Penn 6/16/17
Robert Pastorelli 6/21/54	Sean Penn 8/17/60
George Pataki 6/24/45	J.C. Penny 9/16/1875
Jerry Pate 9/16/53	Joe Penny................................... 9/14/56
Joe Paterno 12/21/26	George Peppard 10/1/28
Mandy Patinkin 11/30/52	Claude Pepper 9/8/00
Dennis Patrick 3/14/18	Charles Percy 9/27/19
Gail Patrick 6/20/11	Walker Percy 5/28/16
Floyd Patterson 1/4/35	Will Perdue 8/29/65
George Patton 11/11/1885	S.J. Perelman 2/1/04
Les Paul 6/9/16	Shimon Peres 8/16/23
Jane Pauley 10/31/50	Anthony Perkins 4/4/32
Linus Pauling 2/28/01	Carl Perkins 4/9/32
Pat Paulsen................................ 7/6/27	Elizabeth Ann Perkins............ 11/18/60
Pope John Paul II 5/18/20	Marlin Perkins 3/28/05
Marisa Pavan 6/19/32	Millie Perkins 5/12/40
Luciano Pavarotti 10/12/35	Ray Perkins 11/6/41
Corey Pavin 11/16/59	Sam Perkins 6/14/61
John Paxson 9/29/60	Itzhak Perlman 8/31/45

Rhea Perlman	3/31/46
Ron Perlman	4/13/50
Eva Peron	5/7/19
Juan Peron	10/8/1895
H. Ross Perot	6/27/30
Gigi Perreau	2/6/41
Valerie Perrine	9/3/43
Gaylord Perry	9/15/38
Luke Perry	10/11/65
Steve Perry	1/22/49
William Perry	12/16/62
William J. Perry	10/11/27
Nehemiah Persoff	8/14/20
Joe Pesci	2/9/43
Donna Pescow	3/24/54
Peter the Great	6/9/1672
Bernardetts Peters	2/28/48
Brock Peters	7/2/27
Jean Peters	10/15/26
Roberta Peters	5/4/30
Tom Peters	11/7/42
Virginia Peters	7/15/24
Oscar Peterson	8/15/25
Roger Tory Peterson	8/28/08
Daniel Mannix Petrie	11/26/20
Rico Petrocelli	6/27/43
Joanna Pettet	11/16/44
Richard Petty	7/2/37
Tom Petty	10/20/52
Michelle Pfeiffer	4/29/58
Regis Philbin	8/25/33
Prince Philip	6/10/21
Caryl Phillips	3/13/58
Chynna Phillips	2/12/68
Julia Miller Phillips	4/7/44
Lou Diamond Phillips	2/17/62
MacKenzie Phillips	11/10/59
Michell Phillips	4/6/44
Tony Phillips	4/25/59
Regis Phibin	8/25/33
River Phoenix	8/23/70
Jean Piaget	8/9/1896
Pablo Picasso	10/25/1881
Paloma Picasso	4/19/49

Slim Pickens	6/29/19
T. Boone Pickens	5/22/28
Wilson Pickett	3/18/41
Jack Pickford	8/18/1896
Mary Pickford	4/8/1894
Molly Picon	2/28/1898
Walter Pidgeon	9/23/1897
David Hyde Pierce	4/3/59
Mary Pierce	1/15/75
Webb Pierce	8/8/26
Marge Piercy	3/31/36
Lou Pinella	8/28/43
Miguel Pinero	12/19/46
Sir Harold Pinter	10/10/30
Ezio Pinza	5/18/1892
Scottie Pippen	9/25/65
George Pirkle	9/3/47
Joe Piscopo	6/17/51
Richard Pitino	9/18/52
Brad Pitt	12/18/64
Zasu Pitts	1/3/1898
Robert Plant	8/20/48
Sylvia Plath	10/27/32
Dana Plato	11/7/64
Gary Player	11/1/35
Donald Pleasence	10/5/19
Suzanne Pleshette	1/31/37
George Plimpton	3/18/27
Martha Plimpton	11/16/70
Maya Plisetskaya	11/20/25
Joan Plowright	10/28/29
Amanda Plummer	3/23/57
Christopher Plummer	12/13/29
Jim Plunkett	12/3/47
Edgar Allen Poe	1/19/1809
John Poindexter	8/12/36
Bonnie Pointer	7/11/51
Sidney Poitier	2/20/27
Roman Polanski	8/18/33
James Polk	11/2/1795
Sidney Pollack	7/1/34
Tracy Pollan	6/22/62
Michael J. Pollard	5/30/39
Jackson Pollock	1/28/12

Lily Pons	4/12/04
Carlo Ponti	12/11/13
Iggy Pop	4/21/47
Faith Popcorn	5/11/43
Paulina Porizkova	4/9/65
Cole Porter	6/9/1892
Katherine Ann Porter	5/15/1894
Sylvia Porter	6/18/13
Terry Porter	4/8/63
Emily Post	10/30/1873
Wally Post	7/9/29
Wiley Post	11/22/00
Tom Poston	10/17/27
Beatrix Potter	7/5/1866
Dennis Potter	5/17/35
Annie Potts	10/28/52
Ezar Pound	10/30/1885
C.C.H. Pounder	12/25/52
Alvin Poussaint	5/15/34
Maury Povich	1/17/39
Boog Powell	8/17/41
Colin Powell	4/5/37
Dick Powell	11/14/04
Eleanor Powell	11/21/11
Jane Powell	4/1/28
Jody Powell	9/30/43
William Powell	7/29/1892
Adam Clayton Powell, Jr.	11/29/08
Lewis Powell, Jr.	9/19/07
Tyrone Power	5/5/14
Francis Gary Powers	8/17/29
Hiram Powers	6/29/1805
Mala Powers	12/20/31
Stefanie Powers	11/2/42
Otto Preminger	12/5/06
Paula Prentiss	3/4/39
Elvis Presley	1/8/35
Lisa Marie Presley	2/1/68
Priscilla Presley	5/24/45
Billy Preston	9/9/46
Kelly Preston	10/13/62
Robert Preston	6/8/18
Andre Previn	4/6/29
Alan Price	4/19/42
Dennis Price	6/23/15
Leontyne Price	2/10/27
Mark Price	2/16/64
Nicholas Price	1/28/57
Ray Price	1/12/26
Richard Price	10/12/49
Vincent Price	5/27/11
Charley Pride	3/8/38
Jason Priestley	8/28/69
Louis Prima	12/7/12
Prince	6/7/58
Harold Prince	1/30/28
Victoria Principal	1/3/50
Andrew Prine	2/14/36
John Prine	10/10/46
Freddie Prinze	6/22/54
Bob Probert	6/5/65
Sergei Prokofiev	4/23/1891
Robert Joseph Prosky	12/13/30
Annie E. Proulx	8/22/35
Marcel Proust	7/10/1871
Dorothy Provine	1/20/37
Juliet Prowse	9/25/36
William Proxmire	11/11/15
Paul Prudhomme	7/13/40
Jonathan Pryce	6/1/47
Richard Pryor	12/1/40
Emilio Pucci	11/20/14
Giacomo Puccini	12/22/1858
Kirby Puckett	3/14/61
Tito Puente	4/20/23
Joseph Pulitzer	4/10/1847
Keshia Knight Pulliam	4/9/79
Edmond Purdom	12/19/24
Alexander Pushkin	6/6/1799
David Puttnam	2/25/41
Mario Puzo	10/15/20
Denver Pyle	5/11/20
Ernie Pyle	8/3/00
Thomas Pynchons	5/8/37

Q

Dennis Quaid 4/9/54
Randy Quaid 5/11/50
Anna Quayle............................. 10/6/36
Anthony Quayle 9/7/13
Dan Quayle................................. 2/4/47
Ellery Queen 10/20/05
Mae Questel 9/13/08
Anna Quindlen 7/8/53
Karen Ann Quinlan 3/29/54
Aidan Quinn.............................. 3/8/59
Anthony Quinn 4/21/16
Sally Quinn 7/1/41
Dionne Quintuplets 5/28/34
Dan Quisenberry...................... 2/7/54

R

Ellis Rabb 6/20/30
Eddie Rabbitt 11/27/41
David Rabe 3/10/40
Yitzhak Rabin 3/1/22
Owen Rachleff 7/16/34
Sergei Rachmaninoff 4/1/1873
Jean Racine........................... 12/21/1639
Gilda Radner 6/28/46
Lee Radziwell 3/3/33
Charlotte Rae 4/26/26
Raffi.. 7/8/48
Deborah Raffin 3/13/54
Alan Rafkin 7/23/28
George Raft 9/26/1895
Luise Rainer 1/12/12
Prince Rainer 5/31/23
Claude Rains........................... 11/9/1889
Tim Rains 9/16/59
Bonnie Raitt 11/8/49

John Raitt..................................... 1/19/17
Vera Ralston 7/12/19
Cyril Ramaphosa 11/17/52
Kurt Rambis 2/25/58
Harold Ramis 11/21/44
Jean-Pierre Rampal 7/1/22
Charlotte Rampling 2/5/46
Gustavus Ramsay 2/2/37
Ayn Rand 2/2/05
Sally Rand 1/2/00
Tony Randall 2/26/24
John Randolph, Jr...................... 6/1/15
Charles Rangel 6/11/38
Raphael.................................... 3/28/1483
Sally Jessy Raphael 2/25/43
Ahmad Rashad....................... 11/19/49
Phylica Rashad 6/19/48
Basil Rathbone...................... 6/13/1892
Dan Rather 10/31/31
Gregory Ratoff....................... 4/20/1893
Terence Rattigan 6/10/11
John Ratzenberger 4/6/47
Herman Raucher...................... 4/13/28
Robert Rauschenberg 10/22/25
Simon Raven........................... 12/28/27
Marjorie Kinnan Rawlings 8/8/1896
Lou Rawls 12/1/36
Aldo Ray 9/25/26
Johnny Ray.................................. 1/10/27
Nicholas Ray 8/7/11
Gene Rayburn........................... 12/22/17
Martha Raye 8/27/16
Alex Raymond 10/2/09
Gene Raymond 8/13/08
Guy Raymond 7/1/11
Charles Reade.......................... 6/8/1814
Maureen Reagan 1/4/41
Nancy Reagan 7/6/21
Ron Reagan 5/21/58
Ronald Reagan 2/6/11
Harry Reasoner 4/17/23
Bebe Rebozo............................ 11/16/12
Otis Redding................................ 9/9/41
Helen Reddy 10/25/41

Robert Redford 8/18/37
Lynn Redgrave 3/8/43
Michael Redgrave 3/20/08
Vanessa Redgrave 1/30/37
Sumner Redstone 5/27/23
Alaina Reed 11/10/46
Andre Reed 1/29/64
Carol Reed 12/30/06
Donna Reed 1/27/21
Jerry Reed 3/20/37
Lou Reed 3/2/44
Oliver Reed 2/13/38
Pamela Reed 4/2/49
Ralph Reed 6/24/61
Rex Reed 10/2/40
Robert Reed 10/19/32
Walter Reed 9/13/1851
Willis Reed 6/25/42
Della Reese 7/6/32
Pee Wee Reese 7/23/18
Christopher Reeve 9/25/52
Dan Reeves 1/19/44
George Reeves 4/6/14
Keanu Reeves 9/2/64
Martha Reeves 7/18/41
Regine 12/26/29
William Rehnquist 10/1/24
Robert Reich 6/24/46
Wilhelm Reich 3/24/1897
J.R. Reid 3/31/68
Tim Reid 12/19/44
Wallace Reid 4/15/1891
Charles Nelson Reilly 1/13/31
Carl Reiner 3/20/22
Fritz Reiner 12/19/1888
Rob Reiner............................. 3/6/47
Ann Reinking 11/10/49
Paul Reiser 3/30/57
Ivan Reitman 10/27/46
Erich Remarque...................... 6/22/1898
Lee Remick............................ 12/14/35
Frederic Remington 10/4/1861
Duncan Renaldo...................... 4/23/04
Ruth Rendell 2/17/30

Michael Rennie........................ 8/25/09
Janet Reno 7/21/38
Auguste Renoir 2/25/1841
Jean Renoir 9/15/1894
Samuel Reshevsky 11/26/11
Regina Resnik 8/20/22
James Reston........................... 11/3/09
Mary Lou Retton 1/24/68
David Reuben 11/29/33
Walter Reuther 9/1/07
Marice Revel 3/7/1875
Paul Revere 1/1/1735
Clive Revill 4/18/30
Charles Revson....................... 10/11/06
Fernando Rey 9/20/17
Burt Reynolds 2/11/36
Butch Reynolds 6/8/64
Debbie Reynolds 4/1/32
Marjorie Reynolds 8/12/21
Cecil Rhodes 7/5/1853
Nick Rhodes 6/8/62
Ray Rhodes 10/20/52
Madlyn Rhue 10/3/34
Willie Ribbs............................ 1/3/56
Anne Rice 10/4/41
Elmer Rice 9/28/1892
Glen Rice 5/28/67
Jerry Rice 10/13/62
Jim Rice................................. 3/8/53
Adam Rich 10/12/68
Buddy Rich 6/30/17
Charlie Rich 12/14/32
Irene Rich 10/13/1891
Richard III 10/2/1452
Richard the Loin Hearted 9/8/1157
Little Richard 12/25/35
Ann Richards.......................... 9/1/33
Ann Richards (Actress) 12/20/18
Burt Richards.......................... 5/29/30
Keith Richards 12/18/43
Michael Richards 7/24/49
Renee Richards 8/19/34
Miranda Richardson 3/3/58
Natasha Richardson 5/11/63

Ralph Richardson	12/19/02
Tony Richardson	6/5/29
Lionel Richie	6/27/49
Mordecai Richler	1/27/31
Peter Mark Richman	4/16/27
Eddie Rickenbacker	10/8/1890
Branch Rickey	12/20/1881
Don Rickles	5/8/26
Hyman Rickover	1/27/00
Nelson Riddle	6/1/21
Sally Ride	5/26/51
Matthew Ridgway	3/3/1895
Leni Riefenstahl	8/22/02
Peter Riegert	4/11/47
Cathy Rigby	12/12/52
Diana Rigg	7/20/38
John Riggins	8/4/49
Bobby Riggs	2/25/18
Jeannie C. Riley	10/19/45
Pat Riley	3/20/45
Nikolai Rimsky-Korsakov	3/18/1844
Kathy Rinald	3/24/67
Faith Ringgold	10/8/30
Charles Ringling	12/2/1863
Molly Ringwald	2/18/68
Cal Ripken, Jr.	8/24/60
Cal Ripken, Sr.	12/17/35
Alexandra Ripley	1/8/34
Robert Ripley	12/25/1893
Cyril Ritchard	12/1/1897
Michael Ritchie	11/28/38
John Ritter	9/17/48
Tex Ritter	1/12/07
Thelma Ritter	2/14/05
Chita Rivera	1/23/33
Diego Rivera	12/8/1886
Geraldo Rivera	7/3/43
Doc Rivers	10/13/61
Joan Rivers	6/8/33
Johnny Rivers	11/7/42
Phil Rizzuto	9/25/18
Hal Roach	1/14/1892
Jason Robards, Jr.	7/26/22
Charles Robb	6/26/39

Harold Robbins	5/21/16
Jerome Robbins	10/11/16
Marty Robbins	9/26/25
Tim Robbins	10/16/58
Tom Robbins	7/22/36
Cokie Roberts	12/27/43
Doris Roberts	11/4/30
Eric Roberts	4/18/56
Fred Roberts	7/22/62
Julia Roberts	10/28/67
Marcus Roberts	8/17/63
Oral Roberts	1/24/18
Pernell Roberts	5/18/30
Rachel Roberts	9/20/27
Tony Roberts	10/22/39
Cliff Robertson	9/9/25
Dale Robertson	7/14/23
Oscar Robertson	11/24/38
Pat Robertson	3/22/30
Paul Robeson	4/9/1898
Bojangles Robinson	5/25/1878
Brooks Robinson	5/18/37
David Robinson	8/6/65
Eddie Robinson	2/12/19
Edward G. Robinson	12/12/1893
Frank Robinson	8/31/35
Glen Robinson	1/10/73
Holly Robinson	9/18/64
Jackie Robinson	1/31/19
John Robinson	7/25/35
Max Robinson	5/1/39
Smokey Robinson	2/19/40
Sugar Ray Robinson	5/3/21
Reggie Roby	7/30/61
Alex Rocco	2/29/36
Chris Rock	2/7/66
John Rock	3/24/1890
David Rockefeller	6/12/15
John D. Rockefeller	7/8/1839
Nelson Rockefeller	7/8/08
John D. Rockefeller IV	6/18/37
Knute Rockne	3/4/1888
Norman Rockwell	2/3/1894
Gene Roddenbery	8/19/21

Bill Rodgers	12/23/47	Axl Rose	2/6/62
Buck Rodgers	8/16/38	Billy Rose	9/6/1899
Richard Rodgers	7/28/02	Charlie Rose	1/5/42
Auguste Rodin	11/4/1840	Pete Rose	4/14/41
Dennis Rodman	5/15/61	Tokyo Rose	7/4/16
Chi Chi Rodriguez	10/23/35	Roseanne	11/3/52
Tommy Roe	5/9/42	Al Rosen	2/29/24
John A. Roebling	6/12/1806	Ethel Rosenberg	9/28/15
Nicolas Roeg	8/15/28	Julius Rosenberg	5/12/18
Carolyne Roehm	5/7/51	Stuart Rosenberg	8/11/27
William Roerick	12/17/12	Ken Rosewall	11/2/34
Mr. (Fred) Roger	3/20/28	Betsy Ross	1/1/1752
Peter Mark Roger	1/18/1779	Diana Ross	3/26/44
Buddy Rogers	8/13/04	Fredrick Ross	5/22/34
Ginger Rogers	7/16/11	Herbert Ross	5/13/27
Kenny Rogers	8/21/38	Marion Ross	10/25/28
Mimi Rogers	1/27/56	Katharine Ross	1/29/43
Roy Rogers	11/5/12	Isabella Rossellini	6/18/52
Wayne Rogers	4/7/33	Roberto Rossellini	5/8/06
Will Rogers	11/4/1879	Robert Rossen	3/16/08
Felix Rohatyn	5/29/28	Gioacchino Rossini	2/29/1792
Eric Rohmer	4/4/22	Judith Rossner	3/1/35
Gilbert Roland	12/11/05	Edmond Rostand	4/1/1868
Ruth Roland	8/26/1892	Irwin Rosten	9/10/24
Ester Rolle	11/8/33	Leo Rosten	4/11/08
Betty Rollin	1/3/36	Dan Rostenkowski	1/2/28
Howard Rollins	10/17/50	David Lee Roth	10/10/55
Sonny Rollins	9/7/30	Lillian Roth	12/13/10
Tree Rollins	6/16/55	Philip Roth	3/19/33
Ruth Roman	12/22/24	Mark Rothko	9/25/03
Sigmund Romberg	7/29/1887	Richard Roundtree	9/7/42
Roy Romer	10/31/28	Jean Jacques Rousseau	6/28/1712
Cesar Romero	2/15/07	Jean-Louis Roux	5/18/23
Erwin Rommel	11/15/1891	Carl T. Rowan	8/11/25
George Romney	7/8/07	Dan Rowan	7/2/22
Linda Ronstadt	7/15/46	Gena Rowlands	6/19/36
Andy Rooney	1/14/19	Mike Royko	9/19/32
Mickey Rooney	9/23/20	Pete Rozell	3/1/26
Eleanor Roosevelt	10/11/1884	Miklos Rozsa	4/18/07
Franklin Roosevelt	1/30/1882	Robert Ruark	12/29/15
Theodore Roosevelt	10/27/1858	Peter Paul Rubens	6/28/1577
Franklin Roosevelt, Jr.	8/17/14	Anton Rubenstein	11/28/1829
Ned Rorem	10/23/23	Erno Rubik	7/13/44
Robby Rosa	6/27/69	Jerry Rubin	7/14/38

Arthur Rubinstein 1/28/1887
John Rubinstein 12/8/46
Paul Rudd 5/15/40
Anne Rudin 1/27/24
Warren Rudman 5/18/30
Wilma Rudolph 6/23/40
David Ruffin 1/18/41
Jimmy Ruffin 5/7/39
Louis Rukeyser 1/30/33
William Rukeyser 6/8/39
Todd Rundgren 6/22/40
Damon Runyon 10/4/1884
Barbara Rush 1/4/27
Dean Rusk 2/9/09
Joseph Ruskin 4/14/24
Bill Russell 2/12/34
Cazzie Russell 6/7/44
Gail Russell 9/21/24
Jane Russell 6/21/21
Ken Russell 7/3/27
Kurt Russell 3/17/51
Leon Russell 4/2/41
Mark Russell 8/23/32
Nipsy Russell 10/13/24
Pee Wee Russell 3/27/06
Rosalind Russell 6/5/12
Theresa Russell 3/20/57
Bayard Rustin 3/17/10
Babe Ruth 2/6/1895
Ann Rutherford 11/2/17
Johnny Rutherford 2/12/38
Margaret Rutherford 5/11/1892
Susan Ruttan 9/16/48
Buddy Ryan 2/17/34
Cornelius Ryan 6/5/20
Irene Ryan 10/17/03
Meg Ryan 11/19/61
Nolan Ryan 1/31/47
Robert Ryan 11/11/09
T.K. (Tom) Ryan 6/6/26
Bobby Rydell 4/26/42
Winona Ryder 10/29/71
Mark Rypien 10/21/62

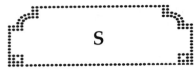

S

Gabriela Sabatini 5/16/70
Rafael Sabatini 4/29/1875
Bert Saberhagen 4/11/64
Albert Sabin 8/26/06
Sabu 3/15/24
Anwar el Sadat 12/25/18
Sade 1/16/60
Morley Safer 11/8/31
William Safire 12/17/29
Carl Sagan 11/9/34
Francoise Sagan 6/21/35
Bud Sagendorf 3/22/15
Carol Bayer Sager 3/8/47
Bob Saget 5/17/56
Mort Sahl 5/11/27
Eva Marie Saint 7/4/24
Buffy Saint Marie 2/20/41
Antonine de Saint Exupery 6/29/00
Raymond Saint Jacques 3/1/30
Susan Saint James 8/14/46
Jill Saint John 8/19/40
Yves Saint Laurent 8/1/36
Pat Sajak 10/26/46
S.Z. Sakall 2/2/1884
Soupy Sales 1/8/30
J.D. Salinger 1/1/19
Pierre Salinger 6/14/25
Jonas Salk 10/28/14
John Salley 5/16/64
Jennifer Salt 9/4/44
Sal Salvador 11/21/25
Richie Sambora 7/11/59
Emma Samms 8/28/61
Pete Sampras 8/12/71
Ralph Sampson 7/7/60
Paul Samuelson 5/15/15
David Sanborn 7/30/45
Ryne Sandberg 9/18/59
Carl Sandbury 1/6/1878

Barry Sanders 7/16/68	Louis Scheimer 10/19/28
Col. Harland Sanders 9/9/1890	Maria Schell 1/15/26
Deion Sanders 8/9/67	Maximilian Schell 12/8/30
George Sanders 7/3/06	Bo Schembechler 4/1/29
Richard Sanders 8/23/40	Bob Schieffer 2/25/34
Scott Sanderson 7/22/56	Claudia Schiffer 8/24/71
Jay Sandrich 2/24/32	Lawrence Schiller 12/8/36
Diana Sands 8/22/34	Walter Schirra 3/12/23
Tommy Sands 8/28/37	Phyllis Schlafly 8/15/24
Gary Sandy 12/25/45	James Schlesinger 2/15/29
Isabel Sanford 8/29/33	John Schlesinger 2/16/26
Margaret Sanger 9/14/1883	Arthur Schlesinger, Jr. 10/15/17
Carlos Santana 7/20/47	Max Schmeling 9/28/05
George Santayana 12/16/1863	Helmut Schmidt 12/23/18
Benito Santiago 3/9/65	Mike Schmidt 9/27/49
Susan Sarandon 10/4/46	Benno Schmidt, Jr. 3/20/42
Vincent Sardi 12/23/1885	Kurt Schmoke 12/1/49
Vincent Sardi, Jr. 7/23/15	Julian Schnabel 10/26/51
(Adolfo) F. Sardina 2/15/33	Stefan Schnabel 2/2/12
Dick Sargent 4/18/19	John Schneider 4/8/54
David Sarnoff 2/27/1891	Maria Schneider 3/27/52
William Saroyan 8/31/08	Romy Schneider 9/23/38
Jean-Paul Sartre 6/21/05	Alfred Schnittke 11/24/34
Vidal Sasson 1/17/28	Arnold Schoenberg 9/13/1874
Van Gordon Sauter 9/14/35	Dr. William Scholl 6/22/1882
Gus Savage 10/30/25	Daniel Schorr 8/31/16
Telly Savalas 1/21/24	Martin Schottenhheimer 9/23/43
Diane Sawyer 12/22/45	Paul Schrader 7/22/46
Steve Sax 1/29/60	Tex Schramm 6/20/20
John Saxon 8/5/35	Detlet Schrempf 1/21/63
Leo Sayer 5/21/48	Patricia Schroeder 7/30/40
Gale Sayers................................. 5/30/43	Ricky Schroeder 4/13/70
John Sayles 9/28/50	Budd Schulberg 3/27/14
Arnold Scaasi 5/8/31	Robert Schuller 9/16/26
Boz Scagg 6/8/44	Dutch Schultz 8/6/00
Gia Scala 3/3/34	Charles Schulz 11/26/22
Antonin Scalia 3/11/36	George Schulz............................ 4/29/25
Jack Scalia 11/10/51	Robert Schumann 6/8/1810
Francesco Scavullo 1/16/29	Ronald Schwary 5/23/44
George Schaefer 12/16/20	Arnold Schwarzenegger 7/30/47
William Schallert........................ 7/6/22	Norman Schwarzkopf 8/22/34
Dore Schary 8/31/05	Albert Schweitzer 1/14/1875
Jerry Schatzberg 6/26/27	Paul Scofield 1/21/22
Roy Scheider 11/10/35	Peter Scolari 9/12/54

Martin Scorsese	11/17/42
Byron Scott	3/28/61
Debralee Scott	4/2/53
David R. Scott	6/6/32
Eric Scott	10/20/58
George C. Scott	10/18/27
Hazel Scott	6/11/20
Lizabeth Scott	9/29/22
Martha Scott	9/22/14
Randolph Scott	1/23/98
Sir Walter Scott	8/15/1771
Willard Scott	3/7/34
Zachary Scott	2/24/14
Gill Scott-Heron	4/1/49
Coretta Scott-King	4/27/27
Renata Scotto	2/24/34
Alexander Scourby	11/13/13
Brent Scowcroft	3/19/25
Earl Scruggs	1/6/24
John Sculley	4/6/39
Vin Scully	11/29/27
Steven Seagal	4/10/52
Bobby Seale	10/22/36
Richard Warren Sears	12/7/1863
Junior Seau	1/19/69
Tom Seaver	11/17/44
John Sebastian	3/17/44
Jean Seberg	11/13/38
Neil Sedaka	3/13/39
Pete Seeger	5/3/19
Erich Segal	6/16/37
George Segal	2/13/34
E.C. Segar	12/8/1894
Bob Seger	5/6/45
Andres Segovia	2/18/1894
Susan Seidelman	12/11/52
George Seifert	1/22/40
Robert Seigel	6/26/47
Rony Seikaly	5/10/65
Jerry Seinfeld	4/29/54
Monica Seles	12/2/73
Connie Selleca	5/25/55
Tom Selleck	1/29/45
Peter Sellers	9/8/25

David O. Selznick	5/10/02
Maurice Sendak	6/10/28
Mack Sennett	1/17/1884
Rudolph Serkin	3/28/03
Rod Serling	12/25/24
Frank Serpico	4/14/36
Michael Serrazin	5/23/40
William Sessions	5/27/30
George Seurat	12/2/1859
Dr. Seuss	3/2/04
Eric Sevareid	11/26/12
Doc Severinsen	7/7/27
Jane Seymour	2/15/51
Stephanie Seymour	7/23/68
Ted Shackelford	6/23/46
Paul Shaffer	11/28/49
Peter Shaffer	5/15/26
Steve Shagan	10/25/27
William Shakespeare	4/23/1564
Tupac Shakur	6/16/71
Yitzhak Shamir	11/3/14
Shanice	5/14/73
Garry Shandling	11/29/49
Bob Shane	2/1/34
Ntozake Shange	10/18/48
Omar Sharif	10/10/32
Jack Sharkey	10/6/02
Sterling Sharpe	4/6/65
William Shatner	3/22/31
Artie Shaw	5/23/10
Bernard Shaw	5/22/40
Dick Shaw	12/1/23
George Bernard Shaw	7/26/1856
Robert Shaw	4/30/16
Stan Shaw	7/14/52
Woody Shaw	12/24/44
Wallace Shawn	11/12/43
Moira Shearer	1/17/26
Norma Shearer	8/10/09
George Shearing	8/13/19
Ally Sheedy	6/13/62
Bishop Fulton Sheen	5/8/1895
Charlie Sheen	9/3/65
Martin Sheen	8/3/40

Sidney Sheldon 2/11/17
Art Shell 11/26/46
Carole Shelley 8/16/39
Percy Bysshe Shelley 8/4/1792
Reid Shelton 10/7/24
Sloane Shelton 3/14/34
Paul Shenar 2/12/36
Sam Shepard 11/5/43
Alan Shepard, Jr. 11/18/23
Cybill Shepherd 2/18/50
Jean Shepherd 7/26/29
T.G. Sheppard 7/20/44
Mark Shera 7/10/49
Ann Sheridan 2/21/15
Nicollette Sheridan 11/21/61
Edwin Sherin 1/15/30
Al Sherman 9/7/1897
Allan Sherman 11/30/24
Robert Sherman 12/19/25
William Tecumseh Sherman . 2/8/1820
Eduard Shevardnadze 1/25/28
Brooke Shields 5/31/65
David Shire 7/3/37
Talia Shire 4/25/46
William Shirer 2/23/04
Anne Shirley 4/17/18
Bill Shoemaker 8/19/31
Toots Shor 5/6/05
Dinah Shore 3/1/21
Paula Shore 2/1/70
Bobby Short 9/15/24
Martin Short 3/26/50
Will Shortz 8/26/52
Dmitri Shostakovich 9/25/06
Wayne Shoter 8/25/33
Jean Shrimpton 11/6/42
Herb Shriner 5/29/18
Eunice Kennedy Shriver 7/10/20
Maria Shriver 11/6/55
Pam Shriver 7/4/62
Sargent Shriver 11/9/15
Gene Shue 12/18/31
David Shula 5/28/59
Don Shula 1/4/30

Richard Shull 2/24/29
George Shultz 12/13/20
Charles Shyer 10/11/41
Sylvia Sidney 8/8/10
Bugsy Siegel 2/28/06
Marc Siegel 12/8/16
Henryk Sienkiewicz 5/5/1846
Ruben Sierra 10/6/65
Simone Signoret 3/25/21
Prince Norodom Sihanouk 10/31/22
Stirling Silliphant 1/16/18
Beverly Sills 5/25/29
Ron Silver 7/2/46
Jay Silverheels 5/26/22
Jonathan Silverman 8/5/66
Phil Silvers 5/11/12
Alistair Sim 10/9/00
Georges Simenon 2/18/03
Gene Simmons 8/25/49
Jean Simmons 1/31/29
Richard Simmons 7/12/48
Ted Simmons 8/9/49
Phil Simms 11/3/56
Carly Simon 6/25/45
Claude Simon 10/10/13
Neil Simon 7/4/27
Paul Simon 10/13/41
William Simon 11/27/27
Nina Simone 2/21/33
Paul Simon (Senator) 11/29/28
Carole Simpson 12/7/40
Mona Simpson 6/14/57
Nicole Brown Simpson 5/10/59
O.J. Simpson 7/9/47
Valerie Simpson 8/26/46
Wallis Simpson 6/19/1896
Billy Sims 9/18/55
Frank Sinatra 12/12/15
Nancy Sinatra, Jr. 6/8/40
Madge Sinclair 4/28/40
Upton Sinclair 9/20/1818
Isaac Singer 10/27/1811
Isaac Bushevis Singer 7/14/04
Mike Singletary 10/9/58

John Singleton 1/6/68	Lois Smith 11/3/30
Penny Singleton 9/15/08	Maggie Smith 12/28/34
Sirhan Sirhan 3/19/44	Margaret Chase Smith 12/14/1897
John Sirica 3/19/04	Ozzie Smith 12/26/54
Gene Siskel 1/26/46	Patti Smith 12/31/46
Ricky Skagg 7/18/54	Red Smith 9/25/05
Red Skelton 7/18/13	Roger Smith 12/18/32
Tom Skerrit 8/25/33	Stan Smith 12/14/46
Scott Skiles 3/5/64	Steve Smith 3/31/69
B.F. Skinner 3/20/04	Wil Smith 9/25/68
Cornelia Otis Skinner 5/30/01	Willi Smith 2/29/48
Otis Skinner 6/28/1858	William Smith 3/24/33
Bernard Slade 5/2/30	Jimmy Smits 7/9/58
Christian Slater 8/18/69	John Smoltz 5/15/67
Helen Slater 12/15/63	Dick Smothers 11/20/38
Donald Slayton 3/1/24	Tom Smothers 2/2/37
Erike Slezak 8/5/46	Reggie Smythe 10/7/17
Walter Slezak 5/3/02	J.C. Snead 10/14/41
Grace Slick 10/30/39	Sam Snead 5/27/12
Curtis Sliwa 3/26/54	Tom Sneva 6/1/48
Jerry Sloan 3/28/42	Dee Snider 3/15/55
Everett Sloane 10/1/09	Duke Snider 9/19/26
Eleanor Smeal 7/30/39	Wesley Snipes 7/31/62
Yakov Smirnoff 1/24/51	Carrie Snodgress 10/27/46
Adams Smith 6/5/1723	E.P. Snow 7/19/05
Alexis Smith 6/8/21	Hank Snow 5/9/14
Anna Dearee Smith 9/18/50	Phoebe Snow 7/17/52
Bessie Smith 4/15/1894	Lord Snowdon 3/7/30
Bruce Smith 6/18/63	Olympia J. Snowe 2/21/47
Bubba Smith 2/28/45	Tom Snyder 5/12/36
C. Aubrey Smith 7/21/1863	Steven Soderbergh 1/14/63
Charles Smith 716/65	Stephen Solarz 9/12/40
Dean Smith 2/28/31	Sir George Solti 10/21/12
Emmitt Smith 5/15/69	Alexander Solzhenitsyn 12/11/18
Harry Smith 8/21/51	Brett Somers 7/11/27
Howard K. Smith 5/12/14	Suzanne Somers 10/16/46
Ian Smith 4/8/19	Elke Sommer 10/5/40
Jaclyn Smith 10/26/47	Anastaslo Somoza 2/1/1896
Kate Smith 5/1/09	Gale Sondergaard 2/15/1899
Keely Smith 3/9/32	Stephen Sondheim 3/22/30
Kenny Smith 3/8/65	Susan Sontag 1/28/33
Kent Smith 3/19/07	Theodore Sorensen 5/8/28
Lee Smith 12/4/57	Ann Sothern 1/22/09
Liz Smith 2/2/23	David Soul 8/28/43

John Phillip Sousa	11/6/1854
David Souter	9/17/39
Terry Southern	5/1/24
Edward Sovel	3/26/29
Thomas Sowell	6/30/30
Moses Soyer	12/25/1899
Ralph Soyer	12/25/1899
Sissy Spacek	12/25/49
Kevin Spacey	7/26/59
James Spader	2/7/60
Warren Spahn	4/23/21
Albert Spalding	8/15/1888
Boris Spassky	1/30/37
Arlen Specter	2/12/30
Phil Spector	12/26/36
Albert Speer	3/19/05
Aaron Spelling	4/22/25
Tori Spelling	5/16/73
Sam Spiegel	11/11/01
Art Spiegelman	2/15/48
Steven Spielberg	12/18/47
Chris Spielman	10/11/65
Mickey Spillane	3/9/18
Victor Spinetti	9/2/33
Leon Spinks	7/11/53
Michael Spinks	7/13/56
Mark Spitz	2/10/50
Valadimir Spivakov	9/12/44
Benjamin Spock	5/2/03
Dusty Springfield	4/16/39
Rick Springfield	8/23/49
Bruce Springsteen	9/23/49
Chris Squire	3/4/48
Jill St. John	8/19/40
Ken Stabler	12/25/45
Robert Stack	1/13/19
Craig Stadler	6/2/53
Jo Stafford	11/12/18
Lesley Stahl	12/16/41
Joseph Stalin	1/2/1880
Gene Stallings	3/2/35
Sylvester Stallone	7/6/46
John Stallworth	7/15/52
Susan Stamberg	9/7/38
John Stamos	8/19/63
Terence Stamp	7/22/40
Kim Stanley	2/11/25
Paul Stanley	1/20/52
Harry Dean Stanton	7/14/26
Barbara Stanwyck	7/16/07
Jean Stapleton	1/19/23
Maureen Stapleton	6/21/25
Willie Stargell	3/6/41
John Starks	8/10/65
Bart Starr	1/9/34
Kay Starr	7/21/22
Ringo Starr	7/7/40
Harold Stassen	4/13/07
Roger Staubach	2/5/42
Eleanor Steber	7/17/16
Danielle Steel	8/14/47
Bob Steele	1/23/1893
Shelby Steele	1/1/46
Tommy Steele	12/17/36
Edward Steichen	3/27/1879
Rod Steiger	4/14/25
John Steinbeck	2/27/02
David Steinberg	8/9/42
Saul Steinberg	6/15/14
George Steinbrenner	7/4/30
Gloria Steinem	3/25/35
Joseph Stella	6/13/1880
Casey Stengel	7/30/1891
Ingemar Stenmark	3/18/56
John Stennis	8/3/01
Princess Stephanie	2/1/65
George Stephanopolos	2/10/61
Jan Stephenson	12/22/51
Richard Sterban	4/24/43
Jan Sterling	4/3/23
David Stern	9/22/42
Howard Stern	1/12/54
Isaac Stern	7/21/20
Richard Stern	2/25/28
Frances Sternhagen	1/13/30
Andrew Stevens	6/10/55
Cat Stevens	7/21/48
Connie Stevens	8/8/38

Craig Stevens 7/8/18
George Stevens 12/18/04
Inger Stevens 10/18/34
Justice John Stevens 4/20/20
Rise Stevens 6/11/13
Stella Stevens 10/1/36
Wallace Stevens 10/1/1879
Warren Stevens 11/2/19
McLean Stevenson 11/14/29
Parker Stevenson 6/4/52
Robert Louis Stevenson 11/13/1850
Adlai Stevenson, Jr. 2/5/00
Dave Stewart 2/19/57
Jackie Stewart 6/11/39
James Stewart 5/20/08
Martha Stewart 8/3/41
Patrick Stewart 7/13/40
Payne Stewart 1/30/57
Potter Stewart 1/13/15
Rod Stewart 1/10/45
Dorothy Stickney 6/21/00
David Stieb 7/22/57
David Ogden Stiers 10/31/42
Robert Stigwood 4/16/34
Jerry Stiller 6/8/26
Stephen Stills 1/3/45
Sting 10/2/51
David Stockton 11/2/41
Dick Stockton 11/22/42
John Stockton 3/26/62
Dean Stockwell 3/5/36
Brandon Stoddard 3/31/37
Louis Stokes 2/23/25
Leopold Stokowski 4/18/1882
Eric Stoltz 9/30/61
Doug Stone 6/19/56
Dwight Stone 12/6/53
Ezra Stone 12/2/17
Irving Stone 7/14/03
Milburn Stone 7/5/04
Oliver Stone 9/15/46
Sharon Stone 3/10/58
Sly Stone 3/15/44
Steve Stone 7/14/47

Paul Stookey 12/30/37
Tom Stoppard 7/3/37
Gale Storm 4/5/22
Anthony Storr 5/18/20
Harriet Beecher Stowe 6/14/1811
Beatrice Straight 8/2/18
George Strait 5/18/52
Hank Stram 1/3/23
Curtis Strange 1/30/55
Glenn Strange 8/16/1899
Lee Strasberg 11/17/01
Susan Strasberg 5/22/38
Robin Strasser 5/7/45
Marcia Strassman 4/28/48
Teresa Strates 5/26/39
Peter Straub 3/2/43
Peter Strauss 2/20/47
Richard Strauss 6/11/1864
Robert Strauss 11/8/13
Johann Strauss, Jr. 10/25/1825
Igor Stravinsky 6/17/1882
Daryl Strawberry 3/12/62
Meryl Streep 6/22/49
Barbra Streisand 4/24/42
Rod Strickland 7/11/66
August Strindberg 1/22/1849
Elaine Stritch 2/2/28
Woody Strode 7/25/14
Sally Struthers 7/28/48
Gilbert Stuart 12/3/1755
Marty Stuart 9/30/58
John Studebaker 10/10/1833
Cheryl Studer 10/24/55
John Sturges 1/3/10
Preston Sturges 8/29/1898
Jule Styne 12/31/05
William Styron 6/11/25
Helen Sukova 2/23/65
Margaret Sullavan 5/16/1896
Barry Sullivan 8/29/12
Danny Sullivan 3/9/50
Ed Sullivan 9/28/02
Kathleen Sullivan 5/17/53
Louis Sullivan 11/3/33

Susan Sullivan 11/18/45
Arthur Ochs Sulzberger 2/5/26
Yma Sumac 9/10/27
Donna Summer 12/31/48
Pat Summerall 5/10/31
Andy Summers 12/31/42
John Sununu 7/2/39
Jacqueline Susann 8/20/21
David Susskind 12/19/20
Rick Sutcliffe 6/21/56
Donald Sutherland 7/17/34
Joan Sutherland 11/7/29
Keifer Sutherland 12/21/66
Bruce Sutter 1/8/53
Don Sutton 4/2/45
Bo Svenson 2/13/41
Jimmy Swaggart 3/15/35
Lynn Swann 3/7/52
Gloria Swanson 3/27/1899
John Cameron Swayze 4/4/06
Patrick Swayze 8/18/52
Blanche Sweet 6/18/1895
Jonathan Swift 11/30/1667
Pat Swilling 10/25/64
Loretta Swit 11/4/37
Barry Switzer 10/5/37
Carl "Alfalfa" Switzer 8/8/26
George Szell 6/7/1897

T

Mr. T 5/21/52
T-Boz 4/26/70
Vic Taback 1/6/29
William Howard Taft 9/15/1857
Paul Tagliabue 11/24/40
Gay Talese 2/7/32
Maria Tallchief 1/24/25
Constance Talmadge 4/19/00
Norma Talmadge 5/26/1897
Alberto Tamba 12/19/66

Russ Tamblyn 12/30/35
Oliver Tambo 10/27/17
Akim Tamiroff 10/29/01
Amy Tan 2/19/52
Jessica Tandy 6/7/09
Yves Tanguy 1/5/00
Debora Tannen 6/7/45
Roscoe Tanner 10/15/51
Quentin Tarantino 3/27/63
Ida Tarbell 11/5/1857
Jerry Tarkanian 8/8/30
Fran Tarkenton 2/3/40
Booth Tarkington 7/29/1869
Roy Tarpley 11/28/64
Danny Tartabull 10/30/62
Brandon Tartikoff 1/13/49
Larenz Tate 9/8/75
Sharon Tate 1/23/43
Jacques Tati 10/9/08
Art Tatum 10/13/10
Alfred Taubman 1/31/25
Norman Taurog 2/23/1899
Andy Taylor 2/16/61
Billy Taylor 7/24/21
Don Taylor 12/13/20
Elizabeth Taylor 2/27/32
Gen. Maxwell Taylor 8/26/01
James Taylor 3/12/48
Jim Taylor 9/20/35
Laurette Taylor 4/1/1887
Lawrence Taylor 2/4/59
Leigh Taylor-Young 1/25/44
Mick Taylor 1/17/48
Niki Taylor 3/5/75
Otis Taylor 8/11/42
Paul Taylor 7/29/30
Robert Taylor 8/5/11
Rod Taylor 1/11/30
Roger Taylor 4/26/60
Zachary Taylor 11/24/1784
Peter Ilyich Tchaikovsky 5/7/1840
Terry Teagle 4/10/60
Renata Tebaldi 2/1/22
Teller 2/14/48

Edward Teller 1/15/08
Shirley Temple-Black 4/23/28
Lee Teng-hui 1/15/23
Toni Tennille 5/8/43
Alfred Lord Tennyson............ 8/6/1809
Mother Teresa 8/27/10
Studs Terkel 5/16/12
Clark Terry 12/14/20
Randall Terry 4/25/59
John Tesh 7/9/52
Vinny Testaverde 11/13/63
Mickey Tettleton 9/16/60
Irving Thalberg 5/30/1899
U Thant 1/22/09
Twyla Tharp 7/1/41
Margaret Thatcher 10/13/25
Phyllis Thaxter 11/20/21
Joe Theismann 9/9/49
Paul Theroux 4/10/41
Alan Thicke 3/1/48
B.J. Thomas 8/7/42
Betty Thomas 7/27/48
Clarence Thomas 6/23/48
Danny Thomas 1/6/14
Debi Thomas 3/25/67
Dylan Thomas 10/27/14
Frank Thomas 5/27/68
Heather Thomas 9/8/57
Helen Thomas 8/4/20
Isiah Thomas 4/30/61
Jay Thomas 7/12/48
Kurt Thomas 3/29/56
Lowell Thomas 4/6/1892
Marlo Thomas 11/21/43
Michael Tilson Thomas 12/21/44
Philip Michael Thomas 5/26/49
R. David Thomas 7/2/32
Richard Thomas 6/13/51
Terry Thomas 7/14/11
Thurman Thomas 5/16/66
Lowell Thomas, Jr. 10/6/23
Emma Thompson...................... 4/15/59
Hunter Thompson 7/18/39
John Thompson 9/2/41

Marshall Thompson 11/27/25
Mychal Thompson 1/30/55
Sada Thompson.......................... 9/27/29
Virgil Thomson 11/25/1896
Henry David Thoreau 7/12/1817
Richard Thornburgh................. 7/16/32
Jim Thorpe 5/28/1888
Jim Thorpe (Golfer) 2/1/49
Sedale Threatt 9/10/61
Ingrid Thulin 1/27/29
Tom Thumb 1/4/1838
James Thurber 12/8/1894
Strom Thurmond 12/5/02
Cheryl Tiegs 9/25/47
Gene Tierney 11/20/20
Lawrence Tierney 3/15/19
Charles Lewis Tiffany 2/15/1812
Pamela Tiffin 10/13/42
Bill Tilden 2/10/1893
Paul Tillich 8/20/1886
Mel Tillis 8/8/32
Burr Tillstrom 10/13/17
Charlene Tilton 12/1/58
Tiny Tim 4/12/22
Grant Tinker 1/11/26
Aaron Tippin 7/3/58
Laurence Tisch 3/5/23
Robert Tisch 4/29/26
Wayman Tisdair......................... 6/9/64
Marshall Tito 5/25/1892
Y.A. Tittle 10/24/26
Beverly Todd 7/11/55
Mike Todd................................... 6/22/07
Richard Todd 6/11/19
Thelma Todd 7/29/05
Alvin Toffler 10/4/28
Hideki Tojo 12/30/1884
John Toland 6/29/12
Sidney Toler........................... 4/28/1874
J.R.R. Tolkien 1/3/1892
Leo Tolstoy 9/9/1828
Marisa Tomei............................. 12/4/64
Lily Tomlin 9/1/39
Tone-Loc...................................... 3/3/66

Franchot Tone	2/27/05
James Toney	8/23/68
Too Short	4/28/66
Regis Toomey	8/13/02
Al Toon	4/30/63
Peter Tork	2/13/44
Mel Torme	9/13/25
Rip Torn	2/6/31
Dean Torrence	3/10/41
Arturo Toscanini	3/25/1867
Nina Totenberg	1/14/44
Audrey Totter	12/20/18
Henri de Toulouse-Lautrec	11/24/1864
Robert Townsend	2/6/57
Peter Townshend	5/19/45
Giorgio Tozzi	1/8/23
Tony Trabert	8/16/30
Spencer Tracy	4/5/00
Helen Traubel	6/20/1899
Fred Travalena	10/6/43
Daniel Travanti	3/7/40
Mary Travers	11/7/37
Merle Travis	11/29/17
Randy Travis	5/4/59
John Travolta	2/18/54
Alex Trebek	7/22/40
Lee Trevino	12/1/39
Claire Trevor	3/8/09
Pauline Trigere	11/4/12
Calvin Trillin	12/5/35
Jean-Louis Trintingnant	12/11/30
Travis Tritt	2/9/64
Anthony Trollope	4/24/1815
Leon Trotsky	11/8/1879
Bryan Trottier	7/17/56
Robert Trout	10/5/08
Tatiana Troyanos	9/12/38
Henri Troyat	11/1/11
Pierre Trudeau	10/18/19
Francois Truffaut	2/6/32
Harry S. Truman	5/8/1884
Margaret Truman	2/17/24
Dalton Trumbo	12/9/05
Donald Trump	6/14/46

Ivana Trump	2/20/49
Thomas Tryson	1/14/26
Mao Tse-Tung	12/26/1893
Paul Tsongas	2/14/41
Ernest Tubb	2/9/14
Forrest Tucker	2/12/19
Sophie Tucker	1/13/1884
Tanya Tucker	10/10/58
Tommy Tune	2/28/39
Gene Tunney	5/25/1898
Ivan Turgenev	11/9/1818
Cathy Turner	4/10/62
Dain Turner	3/8/70
Ike Turner	11/5/31
Janine Turner	12/6/62
Kathleen Turner	6/19/54
Lana Turner	2/8/20
Nat Turner	10/2/1800
Ted Turner	11/19/38
Tina Turner	11/26/39
Scott Turow	4/12/49
Ben Turpin	9/17/1874
Stanley Turrentine	4/5/34
John Turturro	2/28/57
Rita Tushingham	3/14/42
Bishop Desmond Tutu	10/7/31
Mark Twain	11/30/1835
Boss Tweed	4/3/1823
Shannon Tweed	3/10/57
Twiggy	9/19/49
Conway Twitty	9/1/33
Bonnie Tyler	6/8/53
John Tyler	3/28/1790
Steven Tyler	3/26/48
Kenneth Tynan	4/2/27
Cicely Tyson	12/19/33
Mike Tyson	6/30/66

U

Morris Udall	6/15/22

Peter Ueberroth 9/2/37
Bob Uecker 1/26/35
Leslie Uggams 5/25/43
Liv Ullman 12/16/39
Tracey Ullman 12/30/59
Miyoshi Umeki 4/3/29
Blair Underwood 8/25/64
Johnny Unitas 5/7/33
Wes Unseld 3/14/46
Al Unser 5/29/39
Al Unser, Jr. 4/19/62
Bobby Unser 2/20/34
John Updike 3/18/32
Gene Upshaw 8/15/45
Robert Urich 12/19/47
Leon Uris 8/3/24
Bob Ussery 9/3/35
Peter Ustinov 4/16/21
Garrick Utley 11/19/39
Maurice Utrillo 12/25/1883

V

Brenda Vaccaro 11/18/39
Roger Vadim.............................. 1/26/28
Vera Vague 9/2/05
Jerry Vale...................................... 7/8/32
Richie Valens 5/13/41
Jack Valenti 9/5/21
Karen Valentine 5/25/47
Rudolph Valentino 5/6/1895
Fernando Valenzuela 11/1/60
Rudy Vallee 7/28/01
Alida Valli.................................... 5/3/21
Frankie Valli 5/3/37
Jim Valvano 3/10/46
Bobby Van 12/6/32
Cyrus Vance................................. 3/27/17
Vivian Vance 7/26/12
Amy Vanderbilt 7/22/08
Gloria Vanderbilt 2/20/24

Kiki Vandeweghe 8/1/58
Luther Vandross 4/20/51
Vangelis 3/29/43
Joan Van Ark 6/16/46
Norm Van Brocklin 3/15/26
Abigail Van Buren 7/4/18
Martin Van Buren 12/5/1782
Lee Van Cleef................................ 1/9/25
Trish Van Devere 3/9/45
Miles Van de Rohe 3/27/1899
Mamie Van Doren 2/6/33
Mark Van Doren 6/13/1894
John Van Druten 6/1/04
Dick Van Dyke 12/13/25
Jerry Van Dyke 7/27/32
Jo Van Fleet 12/30/19
Vincent Van Gogh 3/30/1853
Alex Van Halen 5/8/55
Eddie Van Halen 1/26/57
Jimmy Van Heusen................... 1/26/13
Dick Van Patten 12/9/28
Joyce Van Patten 3/9/34
Vincent Van Patten 10/17/57
Melvin Van Peebles 8/21/32
Ricky Van Shelton..................... 1/12/52
Andy Van Slyke 12/21/60
Monique Van Vooren 3/17/33
Edgar Varese 12/22/1885
Jim Varney 6/15/49
Sarah Vaughan 3/27/24
Robert Vaughn 11/22/32
Bill Veeck..................................... 2/9/14
Suzanne Vega 7/11/59
Conrad Veidt 1/22/1893
Diego Velazquez 6/6/1599
Lupe Velez 7/18/07
Vendela.. 1/12/67
Robin Ventura 7/14/67
Ken Venturi 5/15/31
Vera-Ellen 2/16/26
Giuseppe Verdi 10/10/1813
Gwen Verdon 1/13/25
Ben Vereen 10/10/46
Jules Verne 2/8/1828

Shirley Verrett 5/31/33	Jack Wagner 10/3/59
Gianni Versace 12/2/46	Lindsay Wagner 6/22/49
Amerigo Vespucci 3/9/1451	Richard Wagner 5/22/1813
Martha Vickers 5/28/25	Robert Wagner 2/10/30
Gore Vidal 10/3/25	Porter Wagoner 8/12/27
King Vidor 2/8/1894	Ken Wahl.................................... 2/14/60
Abe Vigoda 2/24/21	Mark Wahlberg 6/5/71
Bob Vila 6/20/46	Jonathan Wainwright 8/1/1883
Jean Vilar 3/25/12	Ralph Waite 6/22/29
Guillermo Vilas 8/17/52	Tom Waits 12/7/49
Herve Villachaize..................... 4/23/43	Jersey Joe Walcott 1/31/14
Edward Villella 10/1/32	Jerry Wald 9/16/11
Faye Vincent 5/29/38	Robert Walden 9/25/43
Jan-Michael Vincent 7/15/44	Kurt Waldheim 12/21/18
Majorie Vincent 11/21/64	Lech Walesa 9/29/43
Sam Vincent 5/18/63	Christopher Walken 3/31/43
Bobby Vinton 4/16/35	Alice Walker 2/9/44
Frank Viola 4/19/60	Clint Walker 5/30/27
Virgil .... 10/15/70 BC	Doak Walker 1/1/27
Luchino Visconti 11/2/06	Herschell Walker 3/3/62
Jon Voight 12/29/38	Hiram Walker.......................... 7/4/1816
Paul Volcker 9/5/27	Jimmie Walker.......................... 6/25/48
Voltaire 11/21/1694	Jimmy Walker 2/16/14
Kurt Vonnegut, Jr. 11/11/22	Madam C.J. Walker 12/23/1867
Wernher Von Braum 3/23/12	Mort Walker 9/3/23
Claus Von Bulow 8/11/26	Nancy Walker............................. 5/10/22
Erich Von Daniken 4/13/35	Chris Wallace............................ 10/12/47
Betty Von Furstenberg 8/16/31	Dewitt Wallace 11/12/1889
Diane Von Furstenberg 12/31/46	George Wallace 8/25/19
Baron Von Richthofen 5/2/1892	Irving Wallace 3/19/16
Frederica Von Stade 6/1/45	Lew Wallace 4/10/1827
Josef Von Sternberg 5/29/1894	Mike Wallace 5/9/18
Erich Von Stroheim 9/22/1885	Eli Wallach 12/7/15
Max Von Sydow 4/10/29	Raoul Wallenberg 8/4/12
	Fats Waller 5/21/04
	Everson Walls 12/28/59
	Bill Walsh 11/30/31
W	Raoul Walsh.......................... 3/10/1887
	Ray Walston 11/2/24
	Bruno Walter 9/15/1876
Bruce Wade................................ 7/17/51	Jessica Walter 1/31/44
Virginia Wade 7/10/45	Barbara Walters 9/25/31
Lanny Wadkins 12/5/49	Bill Walton 11/5/52
Lyle Waggoner 4/13/35	Sam Walton................................ 3/29/18

Tony Walton	10/24/34	Andre Watts	6/20/46
Darrell Waltrip	2/5/47	Charlie Watts	6/2/41
Joseph Wambaugh	1/22/37	Heather Watts	9/27/43
Sam Wanamaker	6/14/19	James Watts	1/31/38
Walter Wanger	7/11/1894	Quincy Watts	6/19/70
Joseph Wapner	11/15/19	Evelyn Waugh	10/28/03
Burt Ward	7/6/45	Al Waxman	3/2/35
David Ward	10/24/47	Keenan Ivory Wayans	6/8/58
Montgomery Ward	2/17/1843	David Wayne	6/30/14
Sela Ward	7/11/56	John Wayne	5/26/07
Jack Warden	9/18/20	Patrick Wayne	7/15/39
Andre Ware	7/31/68	Carl Weathers	1/14/47
Marsha Warfield	3/5/54	Dennis Weaver	6/4/25
Paul Warfield	11/28/42	Earl Weaver	8/14/30
William Warfield	1/22/20	Fritz Weaver	1/19/26
Andy Warhol	8/6/27	Sigourney Weaver	10/8/49
Fred Waring	6/9/00	Clifton Webb	11/19/1891
Albert Warner	7/23/1884	Jack Webb	4/2/20
John Warner	2/18/27	Jimmy Webb	8/15/46
Malcolm-Jamal Waner	8/18/70	Spud Webb	7/13/63
Earl Warren	3/19/1891	Andrew Lloyd Webber	3/22/48
Lesley Ann Warren	8/16/46	Chris Webber	3/1/73
Michael Warren	3/5/46	Dick Weber	12/23/29
Robert Penn Warren	4/24/05	Daniel Webster	1/18/1782
Ruth Warrick	6/29/16	Noah Webster	10/16/1758
Dionne Warwick	12/12/41	Lowell Weicker, Jr.	5/16/31
Booker T. Washington	4/5/1856	Jerome Weidman	4/4/13
Denzel Washington	12/28/54	Kurt Weill	3/2/00
Dinah Washington	8/29/24	Caspar Weinberger	8/18/17
George Washington	2/22/1732	Peter Weir	6/21/44
Harold Washington	4/15/22	Tom Weiskopf	11/9/42
Grover Washington, Jr.	12/12/43	Bob Weiss	12/7/18
Albert Wasserman	2/9/21	Johnny Weissmuller	6/2/04
Dale Wasserman	11/2/17	Bruce Weitz	5/27/43
Lew Wasserman	3/15/13	John Weitz	5/25/23
Andre Waters	3/10/62	Bob Welch	11/3/56
Ether Waters	10/31/00	Racquel Welch	9/5/40
John Waters	4/22/46	Tuesday Weld	8/27/43
Muddy Waters	4/4/15	William Weld	7/31/45
Sam Waterston	11/15/40	Lawrence Welk	3/11/03
David Watkins	3/23/25	Peter Weller	6/24/47
Tom Watson	9/4/49	Orson Welles	5/6/15
Ben Wattenberg	8/26/33	William Wellman	2/29/1896
Ricky Watters	4/7/69	H.G. Wells	9/21/1866

Kitty Wells 8/30/19	Billie Whitelaw 6/6/32
Paul Wellstone 7/21/44	Paul Whiteman 3/28/1891
Eudora Welty 4/13/09	Heather Whitestone 2/24/73
George Wendt 10/17/48	Margaret Whiting 7/22/28
Jann Wenner 1/7/47	Slim Whitman 1/20/24
Oska Werner 11/13/22	Stuart Whitman 2/1/26
Lina Wertmuller 8/14/28	Walt Whitman 5/31/1819
John Wesley 6/17/03	James Whitmore 10/1/21
Adam West 9/19/28	Eli Whitney 12/8/1765
Jerry West 5/28/38	Sir Frank Whittle 6/1/07
Jessamyn West 7/17/02	Dame May Whitty 6/19/1865
Mae West 8/17/1892	Kathrynne Whitworth 9/27/39
Mark West 11/5/60	Tom Wicker 6/18/26
Morris West 4/26/16	Kathleen Widdoes 3/21/39
Nathanael West 10/17/03	Richard Widmark 12/26/14
Rebecca West 12/25/1892	Elie Wiesel 9/30/28
David Westheimer 4/11/17	Dianne Wiest 3/28/48
Dr. Ruth Westheimer 6/4/28	Mats Wilander 8/22/64
Donald Westlake 7/12/33	Cornel Wilde 10/13/18
William Westmoreland 3/26/14	Oscar Wilde 10/16/1856
Paul Westphal 11/30/50	Alan Wilder 6/1/63
Patricia Wettig 12/4/51	Billy Wilder 6/22/06
Joanne Whalley-Kilmer 8/25/64	Douglas Wilder 1/17/31
Edith Wharton 1/24/1862	Gene Wilder 6/11/34
Bert Wheeler 4/7/1895	Thornton Wilder 4/17/1897
Jill Whelan 9/29/66	Michael Wilding, Jr 1/16/33
Lisa Whelchel 5/29/63	Andrew J. Wiles 4/11/53
Forest Whitaker 7/15/61	Lenny Wilkens 10/28/37
Johnny Whitaker 12/13/59	Dominque Wilkins 1/12/60
Lou Whitaker 5/12/57	Gerald Wilkins 9/11/63
Barry White 9/12/44	Roger Wilkins 3/25/32
Betty White 1/17/17	Roy Wilkins 8/30/01
Bill White 1/28/34	Dan "Big Daddy" Wilkinson ... 3/13/73
Byron White 6/8/17	George Will 5/4/41
Danny White 2/2/52	Jess Willard 12/29/1881
E.B. White 7/11/1899	Prince William 6/21/82
Jaleel White 11/27/76	Andy Williams 12/3/30
Jesse White 1/3/19	Anson Williams 9/25/49
Jo Jo White 11/16/46	Barry Williams 9/5/54
Karyn White 10/14/64	Billy Williams 6/15/38
Maurice White 12/19/41	Billy Dee Williams 4/6/37
Reggie White 12/19/61	Buck Williams 3/8/60
Theodore White 5/6/15	Cindy Williams 8/22/47
Vanna White 2/18/57	Doug Williams 8/9/55

Edward Bennett Williams 5/31/20	Pete Wilson 8/23/33
Emlyn Williams 11/26/05	Tom Wilson 8/1/31
Esther Williams 8/8/23	Woodrow Wilson 12/28/1856
Hal Williams 12/14/38	Nancy Wilson (of Heart) 3/16/54
Hank Williams 9/17/23	Paul Winchell 12/21/23
Hank Williams, Jr. 5/26/49	Walter Winchell 4/7/1897
Joe Williams 12/12/18	William Windom 9/28/23
John Williams (author) 12/5/25	Duchess of Windsor 7/19/1896
John Williams 2/8/32	Dave Winfield 10/3/51
John "Hot Rod" Williams 8/9/61	Paul Winfield 5/22/41
Mary Alice Williams 3/12/49	Oprah Winfrey 1/29/54
Matt Williams 11/28/65	Debra Winger 5/16/55
Montel Williams 7/3/56	Henry Winkler 10/30/45
Nicol Williams 9/14/38	Irwin Winkler 5/28/31
Paul Williams 9/19/40	Michael Winner 10/30/35
Robin Williams 7/21/52	Kathleen Winsor 10/16/16
Scott Williams 8/21/68	Edgar Winter 12/28/46
Ted Williams 8/30/18	Johnny Winter 2/23/44
Tennessee Williams 3/26/11	Paul Winter 8/31/39
Treat Williams 12/1/51	Jonathan Winters 11/11/25
Vanessa Williams 3/18/63	Shelley Winters 8/18/22
Hank Williams, Jr. 5/26/49	Estelle Winwood 1/24/1883
Fred Williamson 3/5/38	Steve Winwood 5/12/48
Marianne Williamson 7/8/52	Robert Wise 9/10/14
Bruce Willis 3/19/55	Bill Withers 7/4/38
Wendell Willkie 2/18/1892	Jane Withers 4/12/26
Chill Wills 7/18/03	Katarina Witt 12/3/66
Maury Wills 10/2/32	Howlin Wolf 6/10/10
August Wilson 4/27/45	Peter Wolf 3/7/46
Brian Wilson 6/20/42	George Wolfe 9/23/54
Carl Wilson 12/21/46	Thomas Wolfe 10/3/00
Dennis Wilson 12/1/41	Tom Wolfe 3/2/31
Desmond Wilson 10/13/46	Tobias Wolff 6/19/45
Don Wilson 9/1/00	David Wolper 1/11/28
Dooley Wilson 4/3/1894	Bobby Womack 3/4/44
Edmund Wilson 5/8/1895	Stevie Wonder 5/13/50
Flip Wilson 12/8/33	Anna May Wong 1/3/07
Gahan Wilson 2/18/30	B.D. Wong 10/24/62
Jackie Wilson 6/9/32	Elijah Wood 1/28/81
Julie Wilson 10/21/24	Grant Wood 2/13/1892
Lanford Wilson 4/13/37	Natalie Wood 7/20/39
Marie Wilson 12/30/16	Peggy Wood 2/9/1892
Mary Wilson 3/6/44	Ron Wood 6/1/47
Nancy Wilson 2/20/37	John Wooden 10/14/10

Judy Woodruff 11/20/46
James Woods 4/18/47
Rod Woodson 3/10/65
Alfre Woodward 11/2/53
Bob Woodward 3/26/43
Edward Woodward 6/1/30
Joanne Woodward 2/27/30
Thomas Woodward 9/16/25
Sheb Wooley 4/10/21
Monty Woolley 8/17/1888
Ian Woosnam............................. 3/2/58
James Wooten 7/13/37
Tom Wopat 9/9/52
Jo Anne Worley 9/6/37
Irene Worth 6/23/16
James Worthy 2/27/61
Herman Wouk 5/27/15
Fay Wray 9/15/07
Frank Lloyd Wright 6/8/1867
Gary Wright............................... 4/26/43
Jim Wright................................ 12/22/22
Orville Wright 8/19/1871
Richard Wright........................... 9/4/08
Steven Wright 12/6/55
Teresa Wright 10/27/18
Wilbur Wright 4/16/1867
Robert Wuhl 10/9/51
Jane Wyatt.................................. 8/12/12
Sam Wyche 1/5/45
Andrew Wyeth 7/12/17
Jamie Wyeth 7/6/46
N.C. Wyeth 10/22/1882
William Wyler 7/1/02
Jane Wyman 1/4/14
William Wyman 10/24/41
Patrice Wymore...................... 12/17/26
Tammy Wynette 5/5/42
Early Wynn 1/6/20
Ed Wynn 11/9/1886
Keenan Wynn 7/27/16
Dana Wynter 6/8/32

X

Malcolm X 5/19/25
Iannis Xenakis 5/29/22
Deng Xiaoping 8/22/04

Y

Frank Yablans 8/27/35
James Yaffe 3/31/27
Kristi Yamaguchi 7/12/71
Weird Al Yankovic 10/23/59
Yanni... 11/4/54
Caleb Yarborough 3/27/40
Peter Yarrow 5/31/38
Carl Yastrzemski 8/22/39
Peter Yates 7/24/29
William Butler Yates............. 6/13/1865
Gen. Chuck Yeager 2/13/23
Trisha Yearwood 9/19/64
Boris Yeltsin 2/1/31
Garo Yepremian 6/2/44
Frank Yerby 9/5/16
Clayton Yeutter .... 12/10/30\
Yevgeny Yevtushenko 7/18/33
Lee Kuan Yew 9/16/23
Dwight Yoakam 10/23/56
Jane Yolen 2/11/39
Dick York 9/4/28
Michael York 3/27/42
Susannah York 1/9/42
Bud Yorkin 2/22/26
Sam Yorty................................... 10/1/09
Tina Yothers............................... 5/5/73
Young MC 5/10/67
Alan Young................................. 11/19/19
Andrew Young........................... 3/12/32
Brigham Young 6/1/1801

Burt Young 4/30/40
Coleman Young 5/24/18
Cy Young 3/29/1867
Faron Young 2/25/34
Gig Young 11/4/13
Loretta Young 1/6/13
Neil Young 11/12/45
Paul Young 1/17/56
Robert Young 2/22/07
Sean Young 11/20/59
Steve Young 10/11/61
Terence Young 6/20/15
Whitney Young 7/31/21
Henry Youngman 1/12/06
Robin Yount 9/16/55
Steve Yzerman 5/9/65

Jerry Zucker 3/11/40
Pinchas Zukerman 7/16/48

Z

Babe Didrickson Zaharias 6/26/12
Paula Zahn 2/24/56
Jerry Zaks 9/7/46
Darryl F. Zanuck 9/5/02
Richard Zanuck 12/13/34
Frank Zappa 12/21/40
Elaine Zayak 4/12/58
Mao Zedong 12/28/1893
Mai Zefferling 5/24/25
Franco Zeffirelli 2/12/23
Jiang Zemin................................. 8/17/26
Florenz Ziegfeld 3/21/1867
Ian Ziering 4/30/64
Stephaine Zimbalist 10/6/56
Efrem Zimbalist, Jr. 11/30/23
Don Zimmer 1/17/31
Fred Zinnemann 4/29/07
Adrian Zmed 3/14/54
Fuzzy Zoeller 11/11/51
Emile Zola 4/2/1840
Vera Zorina 1/2/17
David Zucker 10/16/47